LETTERS FROM A
HIGHLAND TOWNSHIP

LETTERS
from a
HIGHLAND
TOWNSHIP

by

ELIZABETH AND IAN
MACPHERSON

W. & R. CHAMBERS, LTD.
LONDON : 38 SOHO SQUARE, W.1
EDINBURGH : 11 THISTLE STREET

First Published . . March 1939

Printed in Great Britain by T. and A. CONSTABLE LTD.
at the University Press, Edinburgh

To C. G. BROWN

CONTENTS

SEPTEMBER

I

From Mrs Alice Lockhart, The Manse, Strathmazeran,
to Mrs Maisie Dalgarno, Edinburgh

MY DEAR MAISIE,

Here we are at last, more or less settled in
Strathmazeran. I say more or less settled, but
it's really less rather than more. Of course, the
carpets are down, the beds are up, and the appropriate furniture is in the appropriate rooms, but,
gracious me, how many things are lost! George
is moaning because he can't find a stuffy series
of volumes called *The Lives of the Puritans* (which
he never read anyway); I'm upset because I
can't remember where I packed the clean table-
cloths; and Janet is grimly angry because the
colander is lost. All the same, we got the flitt-
ing over wonderfully. As my pen runs on so,
I had better begin at the beginning, and tell you
about our adventures in that orderly manner

which George has been enjoining on me all the twenty-seven years of our married life.

Well, we had the usual upheaval getting things packed before we left town. It wasn't the packing that was the trouble so much as the realisation that we must discard heaps of things. George, the wretch, didn't mind condemning my favourite pictures to the second-hand shops, and then I retorted by wanting to throw out his pet theological treatises! If it hadn't been for Janet, who gets grimmer, bossier, and more efficient every year, we'd never have made any progress. By the way, I'm thankful Janet decided not to abandon us when we came up here to the Highlands. After all these years together we suit each other fine, and I feel rather patronising when other folk moan over the 'mistress and maid' problem.

At long last we saw the three vans of furniture off and got into our own car and took up the rear. I told you, didn't I, that Strathmazeran is twelve *weary* Highland miles from a railway station? The car will now be quite indispensable, and it's a mercy we've got it. But it was an enormous cavalcade to go scouring through the glen. Rather appropriate, though, and just like the caterans returning from a raid in the south! Only we weren't returning but arriving, and as we were extremely tired we were very thankful indeed to arrive, at five o'clock on a lovely September evening. We spent the night in what remains of the little hotel, which is under the energetic but incredibly hospitable wing of Mrs Urquhart, the hotelkeeper's wife—of whom more anon. I say what remains of the hotel, because it had a fire last winter which burned out all of one end. However, we found a room ready for us, and oh it was clean! And oh it was welcome!

Strathmazeran is just exactly what I'd hoped a Highland glen would be. There's a tiny village, with a post-office, which is also the general store, at one end of the street, and the school and school-house at the other. The manse, with the church a stone's-throw away, is about half a mile west of the village, and farther west again lie two big sheep-farms called Kerrow and Shirramore, whose tenants are also our leading elders. Away at the other side of the village is a small shooting called Cairnbeg. Kerrow and Shirramore are part of a big shooting owned by Matthews, the oil man. I know about the shoot-

ings already because, of course, this is the grouse
season and nobody thinks of anything else but
bags, and brace, and beating—the three B's!

There are several small crofts scattered up and
down, and there are gamekeepers' houses. I
think that disposes of the *physical* geography.
And I can tell you, though it sounds most idyllic,
I'm very much exercised in my mind about how
Janet and I are to manage our shopping. There
are no butchers' shops, no greengrocers, and no
dairies. The post-office-cum-store is a corrugated-
iron shack presided over by a large gentle-eyed
lady positively oozing with charm, but her stock
is of the most primitive. She tells me in a soft
voice not to worry, as there'll be plenty of vans
of all kinds. She says comfortably: 'Och,
there'll be some sort of van every day.' But
what if it's not the sort of van I want? I didn't
like to say so to her. However, I dare say we'll
manage along, though Janet pulls down yon long
upper lip of hers and looks her grimmest.

The manse itself is a darling place and not the
rambling barracks I was half-expecting. When
the Strathmazeran charge fell vacant and decided
to call George I was so thankful, for we neither
of us are as young as we once were and the town

was killing George. Being a thoroughly ungrateful creature, I was expecting a horrid manse in this lovely place. Now that the house has turned out to be a delightful bungalow—not a gimcrack affair, I hasten to say, but a solid, dignified house—I feel very humble over my sins of doubt. The kitchen has a grand little range, so efficient that Janet has not as much as referred to a gas-cooker! Of course, we'll have to have paraffin-lamps. But here I am relapsing into my fatal Martha attitude when actually what is important about the house is its lovely, *lovely* surroundings and views. It stands in a glorious chaotic garden, all catmint and gooseberry bushes, with a few asters thrown in. At the foot of it the river flows, and beyond that stretch miles and miles of moor with the heather in full bloom. Behind us rise the hills, so that by the scullery window we can both wash the dishes and sing the 121st Psalm. The tops of the hills are white every morning, even although it is still warm bright autumn in the glen. Cumbered with many cares as I am too fond of being, yet I am continually finding reasons for running out to the back gate (which swings between two rowan-trees) to smell the heady air. I wish the smell of heather and the mountain air could be bottled and sent to the towns as a kind of elixir!

We haven't had much time yet to meet the congregation. You see, last Sunday was our first one here. Of course, on the day of the induction we met crowds of folk, but I haven't got them sorted out in my mind yet. They all brought me bottles of cream that day—an awful lot of them Port bottles!—so we had a glorious time amongst cream shapes and what not for a couple of days afterwards—in fact, till the cream went sour. On Sunday I tried hard to disentangle the congregation, but as the manse pew is in the very front of the church I couldn't very well turn round and gape. All the men look elderly and extremely dignified and wear plus-fours with stockings exquisitely knitted, and the women are large and placid and fresh-faced.

Speaking of them reminds me I must start a Woman's Guild here. There isn't one at present, and, strange to say, there isn't a Rural here either. I must gird up my loins and get something going for the winter.

Oh, I mustn't forget to say that the only undignified-looking person I've seen so far is our beadle, who is called Willackie Mitchell, I'm told. He's the dirtiest little mannie, with black hair and a black moustache like a door-mat. He wears a coat far too large for him and speaks with a broad Aberdeenshire accent, which sounds very gruff in contrast with the gentle soft speech of everybody else here. Janet disapproves of him extremely.

Now, this is an unconscionable length of a letter, but everything here is so new that I felt I had to talk it over with somebody and chose you as my victim. Janet waits to take this to the post, which goes out once a day at five o'clock in the evening. Aren't we hustlers!

Ever your affectionate friend
ALICE LOCKHART.

2

The Same to the Same

MY DEAR MAISIE,

How kind of you to answer my last letter so promptly! Letters are a great treat here, I can assure you, for they are the only means we have of communicating with the outside world. Phones are non-existent in Strathmazeran.

There is one at the post-office, but I think the only time anyone uses it is when the doctor, who lives fifteen miles away, is needed. I hope none of us are suddenly struck down by illness!

We are now almost completely settled down as regards the house and housekeeping, but I don't think we'll ever be properly settled in this darling but *astonishing* place. I've been meeting lots of people since I last wrote, and they get more and more *fairy-story* with every new acquaintance. Really, I hardly know where to begin. But I think, as befits a minister's wife, I should start with important folk like the elders in the kirk. The leading elders, and the principal men in the glen, are the two sheep-farmers at Kerrow and Shirramore respectively. The man at Kerrow is called Alexander Cameron and the one at Shirramore is Robert Sinclair. Alexander is round about the late sixties, and seems to have *quantities* of money. He keeps almost feudal state at Kerrow, and doesn't he look the part of the baron! He's very tall, very dignified, and as like an old eagle as ever you saw. He is a widower with one son, Archie, who is rather overwhelmed by his chieftain father. At least, I thought so the day George and I were

14

up. We were asked to dinner one evening, and poor Archie sat very mim throughout the meal. All the same, he has his father's own jaw, and I shouldn't think old Alexander gets it all his own way. Kerrow (as we soon learned to call him) spoke kindly but very patronisingly of his neighbour Robert Sinclair at Shirramore. I gathered that he doesn't think much of Sinclair's business ability. But, of course, we came the diplomatic *minister-and-minister's-wife* stunt and refused to draw the old villain on the subject. Kirk affairs are kittle enough to run without feuds between the leading elders.

Sinclair is a round rosy man, rather younger than Cameron and not half as handsome, though his face is awfully likeable (much gentler than dear Alexander's). He doesn't keep up half the style of Kerrow, either, but he has a nice comfortable house presided over by his only daughter, Rose. (He's a widower also.) Rose is too impossibly like her name to be real, and has her father well under her thumb—so far as the house goes, anyway, though I think he'd be completely stubborn when he chose.

The Sinclairs kept the most baleful silence about the Camerons. We mentioned we'd been

up, and they both smiled—from the teeth out,
you know—and George hastily changed the
subject. Another day Willackie Mitchell (our
disreputable beadle) came to our back door,
ostensibly for the church key, though what he
wanted it for in the middle of the week beats
me. However, he took the opportunity of
giving Janet the low-down on the entire glen in
spite of her disapproval. It seems he regards us
as sort of allies because we aren't Highlanders
any more than he is. I'm not sure I like being
classed with Willackie! Anyhow, he told Janet
that the Camerons and the Sinclairs are sworn
foes. Old Alexander used to farm Shirramore
as well as Kerrow, and when he went out he
wangled an enormous price for the Shirramore
sheep from Sinclair. I don't really understand
sheep-farming, but apparently a certain number
of sheep go with the farm, as it were, and the
incoming tenant has to take them over. Since
the beasts are acclimatised to the place the price
is very much higher than if they were bought
in the open market. The long and the short of
it is that the man Cameron is supposed to have
cheated Sinclair badly. Strathmazeran views
this reprehensible business very philosophically,

because Sinclair married the woman Cameron wanted. Did you ever hear of such a mix-up?

The people in Cairnbeg, the farm and shooting at the opposite end of the glen, are called Davidson. They're just the farmers, of course. The proprietor has the shooting, and sometimes lets it as he has done this year. I was out when Mrs Davidson called, so I don't know very much about them except that the folk who have Cairnbeg shooting are lodging with them. There is no shooting-lodge for this particular moor, and when it's let the tenants usually put up at the hotel. Unhappily, there was a fire there, as I told you, and the reconstruction isn't finished yet, though we were lucky enough to be looked after for a night by the indefatigable Mrs Urquhart, of whom I spoke in my last letter.

She is a tiny black-haired black-eyed creature who can't live without speaking—rather like a sparrow with a Highland accent. When emotion overwhelms her, which it is constantly doing, she throws her hands up to heaven and relapses into Gaelic. So you can guess that our relations, though very cordial, are somewhat obscure. But, my goodness, she's kind!

Hardly a day passes but she sends up a small gift to us—a bottle of milk or a pair of rabbits or a cabbage. Her husband is big and fat and slow, with quite the best manners I ever beheld. When he meets me he doesn't touch his cap, but sweeps it off. I tell you, I feel as if I'd been noticed by royalty.

Oh, yes, before I forget I must tell you that I met one of the syndicate that is shooting Cairnbeg—a Bill Armstrong. You know, he married Lalla Grierson's third daughter, Anne. Isn't it a funny little world? Anne is in a nursing-home at the moment, but is getting better, and her husband talks of sending her up here to the Davidsons to convalesce. He tells me that he and some friends clubbed together to take this little shooting and they've all enjoyed it tremendously, though the folk in the Strath are inclined to regard them as not quite *pukka* because they haven't had any grouse drives but have shot over dogs. There are well-defined rules and manners of good society in Strathmazeran, and driving grouse is one of them.

The schoolmaster has been coming up against this convention these last few weeks. Half the scholars take leave of absence and go off to be beaters whenever there's a grouse drive in one of the big moors near here. Of course, I quite see that the children's wages must mean a lot to the parents, but Mackie, the schoolmaster, who is an Aberdonian (like Willackie) with the passion for education of his kind, refuses to allow this convention to come between his pupils and their lessons. Mackie has a dear wife, who is going to be a tower of strength to me in the Guild, which I'm getting going nicely. The reason why there are no public activities at all in the Strath is because there is no village hall. All affairs take place in the school, which is most unsuitable, because, of course, the school desks are too small for adults to sit at. As new-comers we can't very well take the initiative in this matter, but I hope that the folks themselves will give us an opening.

Janet has just come in with this *superb* letter which I enclose. Please send it back to me. What a lovely man Shamus must be! Almost I'm tempted to ask him to fix up the electric plant. I'll have to look out some sort of broken thing for him to mend. Do you think I might consult him about getting my hens? I'm sure by a person of his attainments a question like that would be easily enough solved.

Love from your affectionate

ALICE.

3

From Shamus Munro, Engineer, Knockbuie, Strath-mazeran, to Mrs Alice Lockhart, The Manse, Strathmazeran.

DEAR MRS LOCKHART,

I hope you will not think it forward of me starting off with that, for maybe I should be saying Dear Madam which is etiquette, us never having met except as you might say from a distance on the Sabbath last, when I was third pew from the back, centre row if you happened to look round when you would have seen I was there, hearing with great glory and joy unspeakable the goodly sentiments of Rev. Mr Lockhart your dear husband our new minister for which we are truly glad because he is man after our own hearts. Strathmazeran is lucky having him. A leader in Israel.

I am writing to you, starting off all wrong as according to etiquette, because I am hoping we will soon meet and often for in this glen all is friends. There is too few to be quarrelling if only people would be wise and see it and think in their hearts of the Time when Nation shall speak Peace unto Nation as it says in the *Radio Times* which I get regular. It is of great interest to me specially, owing to the numbers of years I spent abroad of which more later. I am thinking to myself you will have a wireless. They are very good now if they don't go wrong. People sends their sets here if there is trouble with valves or perhaps other components. If there is any repair needed, or for example a bicycle to mend, I learned a sound knowledge of all branches of engineering in my many wonderful travels. Of which more later. I am thinking they would interest you to hear. In the Army too which I was in I got a clear experience of all problems connected with machinery. I have a shop here but it is very rudimentary owing to lack of modern facilities, electric power eckcetra. I mend mangles and wringers also. These are simple work for a man of my wide experience. I do not get scope in Strathmazeran.

You will not have noted yet how dark the

Manse is, you will not observe it till the dark days comes, November. A electric lighting set would be very good. I could instal cheap. Also I have ferrets if Rev. Lockhart is bothered with rabbits on the glebe. Or I will take the rabbiting. Also terriers I have, very nice. I am hoping with all my heart you will be happy in Strathmazeran like we are to have you in our midst. It is a lovely glen though I say it that was born here. I hope we will be meeting soon. I could tell you other lovely places in all parts of the world but not nicer than here.

Now Mrs Lockhart I must close. Excuse scrawl owing to me being better with a tool in my hand than a pen,

Yours respectfully,

JAMES MUNRO, Engineer.

Most of the folks call me Shamus.

4

From William Armstrong, Cairnbeg, Strathmazeran, to his wife, at Gray's Nursing Home, Edinburgh

MY OWN DEAR ANNE,

I am *so* happy to know you are getting really better at last and that this'll be my final letter to you from Strathmazeran, because in five days we'll be together again. Don't I count the days as they go past! Like a little boy waiting for his holidays! Did *you* mark off the days till the holidays when you were at school?

Mind you, I've enjoyed being here, and you've no call to be sad because I was worried about you. Of course I was! But since you took a proper turn for the better (and no pretending to be as right as rain simply to keep me happy!) I have enjoyed the sport. It's perfectly lovely country, and we've had good sport even though I didn't distinguish myself. (The rest of the party have been kind about my bad shooting and said it was due to my worrying over you. Wasn't that nice of them? And they say syndicates always quarrel!) And as for Morrison, the gamekeeper, he's been a perfect pet. He asks about you every day and picks out the best grouse for you; and the salmon you got— he poached it!

We've been ever so comfortable with the Davidsons, who are the most hospitable and charming and courteous people I ever encountered. It was a bit of an imposition really, our planting ourselves on them when the hotel went on fire and couldn't keep us. But would you think we were a bother? No, my dear, if we'd been long-lost and long-loved friends they couldn't have made us more welcome. I'm quite glad to think the money we pay (and it's mighty small; they simply refused to charge hotel terms) will be a little help, for I gather that the times aren't too good for sheep-farmers.

But Anne, my sweet, I'm not going to say a word about the Davidsons, or the country, or anything in Strathmazeran. I'm not going to tell you how bonny it is, nor how you can hear the stags roaring in the frosty evenings, nor anything. For why? Because you're coming straight here to convalesce, and eat porridge and cream and scones with heather honey, and grow as fat as I am, and get the roses back in your cheeks! I won't hear a word against it, I've got it all planned. As soon as I get back to Edinburgh and make sure you're fit to travel —off you go! Isn't it nice of me, and me dying to have you with me all the time? I've spoken to Mrs Davidson and she's planned all the things you're going to have to eat, and she's mapped out all the walks you'll take, a longer one every day, and Margaret, her youngest daughter, is longing for you to come so that you can tell her what people are wearing. And even Alistair Og Maclagan, who is our ghillie, and one of the laziest rascals you ever met, put it to me that 'If you wasn't too great a weight' he might *hurl* you about—if you had a bath-chair with ball-bearings in the wheels. I said that what you needed was exercise, not a bath-chair, and if you brought one I'd ask you to put him in it. What do you think he said then? '*That would be nice!*' Oh, you never in your life met or heard tell of such an idle man as Alistair Og is. He's full of complaints about the most mysterious diseases. His blood is as black as ink! He's lucky if he gets two hours' uninterrupted slumber in a night! And the schoolmaster whips his children if they skip school to go grouse-driving! Isn't that a catalogue of desperate evils?

Well, I'll be home on Wednesday bright and early, and when I get everything ready for you then I'll go down to the Nursing-Home, and if you're looking nice and smiling and glad to see me I'll mebbe take you home with me and *you'll* tell me all about yourself and were they good to you, and *I'll* tell you about Strathmazeran. Did I say in my last letter that Johnny Thompson is staying on until the first week in October to get a shot at the stags when they begin to come in from the forest?

Our sport is pretty well finished now. The grouse are beginning to pack and they're very wild—too wild for me. The only way to get them would be driving, which we can't afford. Did I say that the country is rather put about because we've only shot over dogs, and walked in line? The famous Alistair Og took us very sharply to task about it. He came out one day wearing the sourest expression, and when we asked was it the sciatica or the rheumatism, he said, 'It's time you were making a drive.' I told him we weren't going to drive, at which his face became positively livid. The only thing he does with any pleasure is get angry, though I think he's as meek as a May puddock really. Anyway, he said, 'There *used* to be driving.' Certainly there did, when the laird was at home and shot this little bit of moor from his own house. I told Alistair that we couldn't afford to drive. Now, this is a funny thing. The folk here are the most generous on earth. They'd give their last penny, I believe, if they saw anyone in need. But if you're going to take a shooting you *must* be wealthy. You're a *toff*. It's wrong of toffs to be poor. Alistair said so. 'My boy got three days' driving here last season,' he told me very sharply indeed. I tried to put it off by saying it must be a great help when the children earn a few pounds beating. Naturally, that set him going, and didn't I hear about poor Mackie, the schoolmaster, and toffs who didn't treat a moor the way it should be, spoiling its record on the proprietor and all by not driving and bringing up the bag of grouse to a proper figure!

The simple Highlander's a funny creature. He divides himself clean in two. He gives his devoted friendship to simple humble people like himself, and his services to whoever pays for them. *We've* spoiled things badly. In the first place, I think the folk like us and respect us and feel at home with us. That's quite wrong. We should simply be employers—purses, in fact.

Oh well, when I think of my own affairs, wherein do I differ from the folk? My friends are one thing, my clients another.

Now, my dear, my pen has run away with me. I think Strathmazeran must have smit me with loquacity. You never knew such a place for talk. People love to talk here, and they do it *so* well. You'll like the new minister and his wife; we have mutual friends—but I'll tell you all about them on Wednesday. Do you know, it's not so long till we meet as it was when I started this letter—not by a good bit. Isn't that a fine reason for writing at length?

With love (do I still need to say that when you know it?) from your husband who wearies every minute to see you again.

BILL.

5

From Alistair Og Maclagan, Strathmazeran, to
Adam Mackie, Schoolmaster, Strathmazeran

Mister Mackie! damn scoundrel what for did you whip my boy Andrew? I will put the Cruelty on you! I could make a fine job of you! His wrist was SWOLLED something horrid. If the doctor seen it you would know about it I can tell you. It's a new thing a boy can't go to the grouse-driving earning a little to keep him in boots and clothes without getting flogged. Like a brute beast. Worse! For all the good

28

he gets in your school anyway! Better away! If I had my health and strength I would show you thrashing! Mackie take HEED do not let it happen again! Andrew will be at the driving Monday. I'm telling you!

yours faithfully

ALISTAIR MACLAGAN.

6

From Archie Cameron, Kerrow, Strathmazeran, to Miss Rose Sinclair, Shirramore, Glenmazeran

Honey, can I see you to-night? Usual place, usual time? Jimmy the Post will take back an answer to me—make it 'Yes,' please! Because I adore you.

ARCHIE.

7

From Miss Rose Sinclair to Archie Cameron

Yes! Should I give Jimmy a kiss for you?

ROSE.

OCTOBER

I

Rev. George Lockhart, The Manse, Strathmazeran,
to The Carnegie United Kingdom Trustees

DEAR SIRS,

I understand that you are anxious to encourage the building of village halls in Scotland by the provision of loans and grants towards the cost of such halls. There is a project on foot to build a hall in this very small village of Strathmazeran, which, though it is tiny, does serve a large district. I should therefore be grateful if you would inform me of the nature of the help you give by means of grants and loans towards the cost of building village halls, and if you would also acquaint me with the precise terms on which grants and loans are made.

Let me say ere I conclude that the project for a hall here is still very much in the air, and I write to you in a strict confidence which I am sure you will respect and preserve, for to divulge that I had taken any steps of my own accord would certainly prejudice the success of the scheme, especially since I am a new-comer.

It would oblige me further if you acquainted me with the various activities which in your experience live and thrive in village halls in small Highland townships.

I am,

yours faithfully,

GEORGE LOCKHART.

2

John Thompson, Shooting tenant at Cairnbeg, Strathmazeran, to Miss Aileen Leask, Aberdeen

MY DEAREST AILEEN,

I am awfully sorry my letters have been so scrappy, but really, Aileen, it's terribly difficult. It won't be so bad now that everyone except myself has gone, and I'll have peace and quiet to give you all the news—what there is, because it's mainly sporting, and you're not very interested to hear how I missed easy shots at grouse, or got up morning after morning to scour the hills in search of the deer that never come in.

Of course, there's the small gossip of this quiet district, which would bore you to tears unless you knew the people. *Then*, funnily enough, everything comes to life, and, believe it or not, I take a rapt interest in the new baby up at the shepherd's house at Dalvalloch, and in Mrs Davidson's hens, and whether Margaret Davidson will get a good price for her pet lambs at the sales. I know that whatever she gets it won't be enough to compensate for losing them. They follow her all round the town! There I am, talking as if you were interested too. But the Davidsons really are perfect hosts, and I just wish you could run out to stay a few days. I've told them all about you and they simply crave to meet you. They don't meet so many women from outside the glen, though Bill Armstrong's wife, Anne, is coming from Edinburgh to stay with them for a while and recuperate. She was very ill, poor woman. I'm looking forward to meeting her. Bill was very worried about her, and by what he let slip he thought at one time he was going to lose her—oh, that was a good long time ago, before he came here with the rest of the syndicate. If she hadn't been on the mend he'd never have come. She sounded a first-rate woman by what Bill said—it wasn't a great deal, but you can gather people's character from the way their friends and relations speak of them, can't you?

Well, they say that syndicates always quarrel, but, honestly, ours didn't, and if we can get it we'll take Cairnbeg again. We parted the best of friends, though everyone was jealous of me staying on, with a chance of getting a bang at a stag. I've fixed to stay until the twelfth of October. The deer-forests round about are all very busy then, and often stags come into Cairnbeg just at the very end of the season—good ones, too. In fact, two years ago the best head of the season was killed on Cairnbeg ground, a great wide rough royal. I wish I could get one like it. I'd treasure it for the rest of my life and find an honoured place for it in *our* house —dear Aileen, when are you going to make up your mind and change *my* house into *our* house?

I mustn't forget to say that what makes me madly jealous about this fine big stag is that it was poached by a great hulking lazy fellow of a ghillie, named—imagine it!—Alistair Og Maclagan, whom we've been paying to do, so far as I can see, nothing but talk about his rights

and grievances. Alistair shot the royal with—
oh, most unregal fate!—an ancient ·22 rifle,
and the rascal had the bland audacity to try to
sell me the head for five pounds. He said I
could tell my 'young leddy' that I got it myself
—for, 'Do you see, Mister Thompson, the leddies
admires great hunters, they do and all.' And he
gave me the most knowing look!

Aileen, you're not angry with me for staying
on, are you? Because, honey, this is a chance
I mayn't get for a long time again, and I do love
the hills, and solitude. Strathmazeran is an en-
chanting place. I could live here for ever and
a day. I do wish you'd come down, even
for the shortest visit, because I know you'd fall
under the spell too. The Davidsons would make
you royally welcome, and you'd like Margaret,
she's so quiet, and prim, and little, with the
gentlest ways and eyes. But I told you about
the Davidsons already. Do come! After all,
the Nesbitts' party will be just like every other
party, but there's nothing in the world anywhere
like Strathmazeran at present. We've got a great
huge moon, and at night, when the world's
quiet except for the burns, and the stags roaring,
you feel at peace, which God knows it's not

easy to feel in our world to-day. You feel th[...]
all the uproar, and the cruelty men inflict on
each other, are just for a little while. This is
what lives. The everlasting thing is peace.

I can't really say I'm sorry I'll miss the Nesbitts' party. I'm not their sort, Aileen. I'm a
quiet, dull, plodding fellow. I like the country,
peace and quiet, my own fireside, books. I
know you can make contacts by meeting people.
I doubt if money's worth chasing into that sort
of company. I have my ambitions, but they're
not for sudden success. Things that come on
the wind go on the water. People will come to
me; I won't chase them and *sook* in with them
just because they can give me work—it's folly
in the long run. Anyway, I hate noise and vul-
garity and raffish company and all that passes
amongst folk for the gay life. I wouldn't say
this if I thought you were really friendly with
the Nesbitts and their clique. You couldn't
make true lasting friends of them.

Now, my dear, this is a long letter at last, and
I'll get it posted right away. I think Margaret
is going to the shop-cum-post-office. I'll be
waiting to hear from you. I wish you'd come
here. We could discuss our own affairs quietly;

when we'll be married, and everything. I want our arrangements to be straightforward and business-like. We must stop drifting—I'm so frightened I lose you. Please come! I promise not to deeve you with shooting blethers, even if I get a royal with a head four feet wide.

Ever your adoring

JOHNNY.

3

The Same to the Same

MY DEAR AILEEN,

What in the world have I done wrong? Since I got your letter I've been puzzling and vexing my head, but still I can't discover—what *have* I done wrong? I never dreamed you were so keen for me to go to the Nesbitts' party. If I'd known I'd have gone like a shot, even though it meant cutting my stay here short and missing a chance at the best stag that ever grew in the Highlands. But *you* should have gone. We were invited separately. Honestly, Aileen, I don't see how my not going was an insult to them, or a humiliation for you.

I'm sorry and ashamed if I said things that

hurt you. I didn't know that Mrs Nesbitt was
your friend. I've got to speak the truth; I
didn't like her, and I don't trust her. But your
friends are your own; the last thing I want to
do is come between you and them. When we're
married—you're not changing your mind, are
you, Aileen?—I hope we'll both keep our friends
and not meddle with each other's affairs. A lot
of unhappiness comes like that, and I want us to
be happy all the days of our life.

Of course, the house will be yours to do what
you like with. I wouldn't try to force you to
make it anything except what you'd be happy
in. I never meant—surely I didn't make you
think I wanted to clutter our house up with
stags' heads and Landseers and trophies of such
very small chase as I'm likely to have? My
dear, all I should ever want is a little corner of
my own where I could stick the things I liked
to keep from expeditions like this—and my guns
and rods. Just one small room—an attic—I love
attics. But as for festooning the walls—oh, my
goodness, how in the world did you get that
idea into your silly head?

But you shouldn't be unfair about the Davidsons, Aileen. They're not servants, and I can't

treat them like servants. They're my hosts, and most gracious and hospitable hosts they've been. I'm happy to call them my friends, which I believe they are, and I don't think they give their friendship lightly. Oh, this writing is all so unsatisfactory—why don't you come here and meet them, and then you'd see how wrong you were, imagining I was becoming familiar with people who were really servants? Good heavens, the Davidsons have an ease and grace of manners that would carry them with distinction in the highest society. They are farmers of an old family, my dear, with a tradition of hospitality and a pride in their race, and nothing menial ever grows out of that soil. Besides, they're charming people.

I do *not* despise money, nor make a pretence of despising it either. If there were any urgent reason for my being back in the office I'd go right away. But there's not. What makes you think I scorn success, worldly success I mean? Is it because I'm not always talking about money like some other folk? Are you afraid, if I marry you, you'll be condemned to a life of penury? Why, the thing I look forward to is working for you. We'll have plenty to make us comfortable. We shan't be wealthy—not many architects are; it's contractors who have Rolls-Royces one month, and bicycles the next. I can't give you diamond tiaras. But we'll have plenty. That's better than being in the sky one minute and the gutter the next, isn't it?

Now, my love, please write me at once to tell me that I'm forgiven—or, as I said before, better still, come here. I'm not asking you to come for any reason except I want to see you, and have you to myself for a little while, which I never seem to manage in Aberdeen. I shan't be happy till I get your letter, or see you.

JOHNNY.

4

The Same to the Same

Damn it, Aileen, why the devil should you imagine I prefer the Davidsons to you? Do you think I go round falling in love with every girl I meet? Margaret's a very nice girl, and if I spoke about her more than you thought I should it's because you always say I don't write you long letters, and in a place like Strathmazeran what is there to write about except the people

I meet? I said I'd go to Aberdeen like a shot if there was any business reason—surely you don't mean it when you turn that into my preferring business to you? You didn't object to my coming here—you didn't tell me you wanted me away from here—oh, what's the use of going over and over and over things !—Aileen, are you tired of me ?

JOHNNY.

5

The Same to the Same (Telegram)

Arriving Aberdeen seven tonight Johnny.

6

Alistair Og Maclagan to John Thompson,
Aberdeen (Telegram).

Big stags in Cairnbeg Come Quick Maclagan.

7

Miss Margaret Davidson to John Thompson,
Aberdeen

DEAR MR THOMPSON,

My mother, who does not like writing, asks me to say that we shall be delighted to have

you with us again for another few days. Alistair
Maclagan tells me that he wired you about the
stags which have come in from the forest. We
shall expect you on Monday morning.

Yours sincerely,

Margaret Davidson.

8

*Shamus Munro, Engineer, Strathmazeran, to
the Atlas Drop Forging Company, London*

Dear Sirs,

interested in your advertisement for skilled
engineer. I am skilled in all branches engineering from youth up. I was engine-driver eckceckera in U.S.A. Also assisted many great
engineering feats. I can use tools all sorts, likewise solder, repair machinery, keep costs also.
Testimonials on request. Now in business on
my own. Doing well but always looking for
improvement.

your obedient servant,

Shamus Munro,
Engineer.

9

The Same to The Editor, The Times
newspaper, London

Sir, do you not have a local correspondent in this quarter which I inhabit? It would be a good thing to do so. For example there are shooting parties of noble gentlemen all around whose doings you would like to print for the edification of your many readers.

Strathmazeran is not so big, but it is the dead centre, sir, of a large area comprising many famous scenes of past history, also water-power schemes not far off, and big sheep sales sometimes go on, likewise concerts ect. for local funds which would not interest you. There is word of a hall building which will be a great advantage.

If you do not have a local correspondent it is a great pity and I will be glad to help you by being same. I received a good grounding in grammar from Mr Macdonald late schoolmaster here whom all will praise. Also I travel widely. I know everything going on and could tell you many strange things which would please your esteemed readers,

yours truly,

SHAMUS MUNRO.

10

Mrs Macaskill, Postmistress, Strathmazeran, to
Shamus Munro

DEAR SHAMUS,

If I was at your ear it would ring, let me tell you. Where is the bit of the mangle you took away behind my back three weeks past Tuesday afternoon? I cannot do my washing without the bit you took away. Shamus, it is not right. You promised faithful to bring it back, but not a sign of you. Did you lose it or just broke it? Likely you broke it, that is what I think of you. Or maybe you are so busy hanging round the Manse. Oh, I know you, Shamus Munro, just like all men. Likely there'll be a new maid to tell about yourself and what clever you are and all the strange adventures you saw in places you never was in. I will be seeing her, and the minister's wife too. I will say, Shamus? Och yes, poor thing, and I will tap my head and say He thinks he's an engineer—

oh, he has the clever tongue on him—but look what he did to my mangle with his engineering! And my bicycle! That will sort you, mister Shamus Munro.

You did not stamp the letter you posted to the Atlas Company, London, asking for a job, nor the letter to the Editor, *Times* newspaper, ditto. That is threepence more you owe me for the stamps I put on. That is three shillings and sixpence you owe me now for stamps. If I was doing right I would charge you double, as is post office rules. I am wanting the bit of my mangle back so please send it down. Do not come yourself—I could not trust to keep my hands off you for you are a NO GOOD, and I will tell her at the Manse that, and the Minister's wife too. Breaking the mangle my poor goodman bought for me last thing he did!

NELL MACASKILL.

II

Miss Janet Colthart, The Manse, Strathmazeran, to her sister, Mrs Katherine Hamilton, Peebles

MY DEAR SISTER,

Thank you for your last and the pair of hand-knit stockings enclosed. It was very good of you putting yourself about to knit them and I appreciate it, but I am sorry if my letters made you think this place was so terribly wild and cold that I would need to wear handknit stockings. Strathmazeran is not so cold as Peebles, and although the natives tell me great stories of bad weather in winter I am beginning to see that all I am told is as likely as not all blethers if not lies.

Well, Katie, I am settled down fine now. The house for a wonder is quite easy to run, but I have a big baking to do because there is not a single baker comes past. At least not what I would call a baker. The bread is all right but the cakes are awful. They come from the big multiple shops in London and you know what that is. As we have a terrible lot of callers all needing tea, my hand is on the girdle even on. If you would send your recipe for quick ginger cake I would be most obliged.

You ask me what I do on my day off. Well, Katie, I must say the people here are very kind and I am asked out more than I can accept. Last week I was out to a little croft place owned by folk called Maclagans. Alick Maclagan the man is ghillie to the shooters at Cairnbeg and his wife is a member of the mistress's Guild and

a very quiet bit body but she has no *ca' through*.
I helped her to wash the dishes the night I was
up and I can tell you, Katie, I relish my food
off a plate that's been dried with a nice clean
dishcloth. Mrs Maclagan's dishcloths are—well,
I don't know when they got a boil last. Still
I don't like speaking badly of people who are
kind to me and Mrs Maclagan is a real hospitable cheery soul. For her man Alick he is a
great big handsome fellow but with an awful
temper I think. Anyway he speaks very wild but
maybe he's like a lot of others in this glen, just
a bumbee in a tinnie—all noise and no action.

The mistress is very pleased with Strathmazeran
and it's a good thing she is for I never thought
a town person could settle in such a remote
place as this. She thinks the people are wonderful too. But I don't let on what I think of them
in the generality. They are always at the back
door borrowing and wanting to speak. I never
met such folk to speak. There's two men here
that are a public pest. One is Willie Mitchell
the beadle and the other James Munro who
makes on he's an engineer. Munro is always
coming in past to ask if we have anything to
mend. He tells me he was abroad a lot hunt-

ing bears in Mexico and America and such places. I wouldn't trust him to drive tacks but he's a great talker for all that and very appreciative of my doughnuts. Him and Mrs Macaskill the shop are supposed to be friends so you needn't think anything, Katie! I have no law at all for Willie Mitchell. The way he keeps the church is awful. Last Sunday I couldn't listen to a word of the master's sermon for seeing the dust on the top of the harmonium.

The great thing I miss here is a library. As you know I am a great reader but I must have a good book. The mistress is always saying to take any of her books but they are all too tame for my taste and I do not like to tell her so. Of course being a minister's wife it wouldn't be the thing for her to have any very advanced books such as I like. A good murder is wasted on the mistress. However, Jessie Macdonald the maid in the schoolhouse tells me that a box of books from the Carnegie comes to the school every now and then so I will make further enquiries.

Now before I close I must not forget to tell you about the goings-on of the two leading families here. They are the Camerons and the Sinclairs and they are both big sheep-farmers in the glen and both elders in the kirk. Old Cameron and old Sinclair are at daggers drawn. They are both widowers and Cameron has a son called Archie and Sinclair a daughter called Rose. We weren't very long here when Willie Mitchell told me all about the feud, but what Willie Mitchell doesn't know and won't find out from me anyway is that Archie and Rose meet each other at the bottom of the manse glebe. I was taking a dander to myself the other night before shutting up the sheds (I lock the coal house etc. every night as I don't trust the Highlanders one inch) and I saw the two young things. If it hadn't been for the moon I wouldn't have known who they were. Poor bairns, I don't know what will come of it but I can hold my tongue and if it wasn't that you were hundreds of miles away Katie I would never breathe it even to you. It's a pity the fathers being elders wouldn't take their religion a bit more earnestly and think of their behaviour. But that's men all over. They're full of high-flown notions but practical christianity and them have no dealings. I don't mind saying that's what I think is wrong with the church and the Govt. And Katie we'll never get anywhere with either of these institutions till we have a lot more women at the head of each of them. Men have no sense. I hear you saying 'Oh I have heard Janet on this before' so I will stop.

An hour later.

Sorry I was interrupted before I could finish off this letter but that was one of the hotel maids needing to borrow a half loaf. Did you ever hear anything so stupid in your life? What sort of hotel can it be that hasn't any bread and then can be put off with a half loaf? Of course the baker will be to-morrow. It seems that a new guest has arrived from Aberdeen. She's a young lady and is supposed to be after Mr Thompson one of the shooters at Cairnbeg. Maggie Clunas (that's the girl who came to borrow the loaf) says she's a very stylish looking creature with her lips and her nails painted to match each other. It's a pity some of these flashy madams wouldn't paint their noses as well and then we would all know them for the clowns they are. She will likely catch young Mr Thompson too in spite of her paint. As we used to say, 'Poother and pent hides mony a rent.' That's the bell for prayers so I must really close now. Love to all and especially to wee Jimmie. Peebles will be in a steer just now with the salmon. I heard a lot about the poaching in the Highlands but from what I can see it's nothing to Peebles, or they keep it very quiet. A cut of salmon would taste very nice, poached or not.

your affect. sister

JANET.

P.S.—Be sure to remember the quick ginger recipe as the mistress is having a guild meeting the week after next. There's no church hall here and we have to meet in the Manse dining-room. It's very homely no doubt but an awful scutter. The guild members offer to wash up but I wouldn't trust yon Hieland stots with the best china for worlds.

P.P.S.—Strathmazeran is supposed to be very bonny but it's not a bit bonnier than the Borders.

J.

12

*Mrs Anne Armstrong, Cairnbeg, to her husband,
William Armstrong, Edinburgh*

MY DARLING BILL,

Amn't I good? I've been here nearly ten days and I've written you almost every day, and that's not counting the wire I sent you the day I arrived.

I am still loving it here and the Davidsons are angels of kindness. Margaret is a pet of a girl and she and I are becoming fast friends. You notice I don't say 'have become,' because little more than a week isn't long enough for a shy sensitive Highlander to take a stranger absolutely to her bosom. But, oh Bill, I do like her, with her gentle quiet ways and her unexpected flashes of shrewdness. She and I were invited to the manse the other night for supper, because it's just as we thought, Mrs Lockhart is an old school friend of mother's. You can say the bit about the world being a small place for yourself. We had a delightful evening with Margaret giving us character sketches of the glen folk and sending us into fits of laughter at the Highland worthies. You never told me about the ineffable Shamus Munro, so now I'll tell you. Mrs Lockhart has already had dealings with him. He thinks he is an inventor and an engineer and has written offering to instal a wind-driven electric plant in the manse, if you please. Janet, the manse maid, says the only thing she knows about Shamus's engineering capacity is that he broke the mangle belonging to the postmistress and cannot repair it. Margaret says that when he does anything more than usually outrageous in the way of 'mending' the farm implements at Cairnbeg he tries to throw dust in her father's eyes by telling him thrilling travellers' tales. The last thing he broke at Cairnbeg was a binder which he insisted he was adapting for use with Davidson's new tractor. Old Davidson was justifiably annoyed and was vowing to have Shamus's blood. However, when the villain appeared all full of quips and joy about his own cleverness, Margaret's father hadn't the heart to give him a row. Shamus in return for his clemency told him how once he was hunting a very *very* dangerous bear in America. He was stalking the bear for days, and in order to lull the monster's suspicions he wore a large white sheepskin. The stalk was going ahead in great style, and Shamus had come close enough to his quarry to raise his rifle and draw a bead on the bear's heart—in fact the bear was as good as dead, for Shamus never misses—when suddenly an eagle swooped down on him and being deceived by the sheepskin seized him in its 'talents' and carried him off into 'neutral territory'—Mexico ! When it discovered that its burden was no sheep but the intrepid hunter, Shamus, it hurriedly dropped him into a ravine bristling with savage Indians, whose god he quickly became. He built a water-power scheme for them and irrigated the desert, but the Government became jealous and sent an army against him; so, to avoid bloodshed and international complications, Shamus withdrew. Now, Bill Armstrong, what do you think of that for a tale? I don't think it was any wonder that old man Davidson forgot his wrath. I haven't actually met Shamus yet, but Alick Og Maclagan, your late ghillie and my faithful guide and adviser, tells me he is going to arrange a meeting. He thinks Shamus is wonderful and is very, very angry with his detractors, especially the poor Aberdonian schoolmaster. And I think Alick is wonderful, so we're all happy.

Your friend Johnny Thompson, after various sudden excursions, departures, telegrams, and alarums, is now back at Cairnbeg. He's a nice open-airy creature, though I seldom see him, as he's hunting the wild deer and following the roe most of the time. But I have a predilection for large young men with brown faces and smelly Harris tweeds, which, of course, explains why I married my beautiful Bill Armstrong. Johnny is supposed to have a young woman in Aberdeen, so Margaret tells me. I think this is a grave mistake on his part, as he ought by all the laws of story-books to fall in love with Margaret. You see how I am recovering when I am contemplating match-making.

As this letter won't go till to-morrow now, I'll leave it open and add some more in the morning. Good-night, dear lovely Bill.

Next morning.

Oh, Bill, isn't it tragic? The hunter is hunted and a snake in the grass with a capital S has arrived in Eden, I mean Strathmazeran. It's Johnny Thompson's lady from Aberdeen. I'd better begin at the beginning. This morning just after breakfast (which I'm still getting in bed), I heard a car, and voices. This was Johnny and his Aileen. And, Bill, she's *all wrong*. They were in the sitting-room when I came downstairs. She's tall and very dashing and got up out of a French fashion book. I never thought Aberdeen produced such high fliers, but apparently it does. Johnny introduced me to her, and I could just feel her counting up what my clothes cost. One bright dark efficient glance, and I was summed up—I knew she wouldn't give a fiver for my whole get-up. Just as I could see her casting me into the outer darkness of poor plain things Johnny ingenuously explained that Bill Armstrong, one of Edinburgh's coming business men, was my husband. The bold Aileen did a swift recalculation and flashed a warm and melting smile on me. I could see that, though I might still be a plain thing, I wasn't a poor one. Then the Davidsons, kind dears, brought in tea. Margaret came along with a tray, and plates and *plates* of good home-made things. Miss Aileen waited till she'd set out the things and then announced in a high bold voice that what she took at eleven o'clock was not tea but a dry Martini. Bill, it was lovely. Margaret didn't say a word, but went quietly out of the room and came back in a moment with a bottle of whisky and a great big tumbler and put them down gently on the table in front of Miss Aileen and said in the softest voice, 'I'm sorry we've no Martini, but perhaps you would like a little drop of the hard.' I simply couldn't keep my face straight, and neither could Johnny, who laughed, and oh such a furious glance he got for it from his dear young lady. I bet she made him pay for it. I could have hugged Margaret, who was by a long way the coolest and most self-possessed person there, in her apron and working clothes as she was—and the prettiest.

It wasn't nice or funny really for poor Johnny. It was sad to see him trying to be extra polite to Margaret and attend to this nasty female he's got himself entangled with at the same time. Well, well, we'll see what we'll see. But I've no intention of sitting down and letting Miss Aileen Leask wipe her feet on me and my friends, so, my noble husband, kindly get Sarah to send me on my new black frock and its trimmings (she'll know what 'trimmings' means). I don't know how long Johnny's lady is to stay, but it's as well to be prepared. One satisfaction to me is that Margaret's lovely manners are as good as ten Paris models. Now I'm going to walk to the post office (what everyone here calls the *po-stoffice*) with this, and I'll ruminate as I go on Johnny's stupidity and my own husband's cleverness and kindness and altogether satisfactoriness. I still love you frantically.

Your ANNE.

NOVEMBER

I

From Rev. George Lockhart, The Manse, Strath-
mazeran, to The Carnegie United Kingdom
Trustees.

DEAR SIRS,

I am obliged by your prompt and helpful
reply to my letter requesting information about
the aid you provide towards the construction
of village halls.

We hope to hold a public meeting in the immediate future at which the points you raise will
be discussed and, I trust, satisfactorily answered.
In the meantime, and in view of the forthcoming
meeting, will you inform me how your grants
and loans are affected when an architect provides
his services gratis, and when the work of construction is carried through by voluntary labour?

I am,

yours faithfully,

GEORGE LOCKHART.

2

The Same to Adam Mackie, Schoolmaster, Strathmazeran

DEAR MR MACKIE,

Please forgive my writing when I should really have called on you, but I am confined to the manse with a bout of cold and dare not venture out in the inclement though seasonable weather.

I enclose the replies I have received from the Carnegie Trustees, to which may I add these comments :—

1. They provide a grant of one-third and a loan of one-third towards the cost of an approved hall for villages of less than 400 souls—as Strathmazeran is. Our policy should be to keep the loan as small as possible, even although it is free of interest.

2. We must satisfy them that there is a need and demand for a hall, and sufficient of a population to justify its erection; also, that when it is built it will be made full and proper use of. These are most reasonable conditions. It is not enough to have a hall which is used solely for dances, as some villages have.

3. We must submit our plans for the hall, properly executed by a qualified engineer or architect, together with an estimate of the cost.

4. We must have security of tenure for the land on which the hall is to be built. That amounts to our requiring a feu. I question if the Carnegie Trustees would approve a lease, unless it was perpetual.

These are, briefly, their conditions. As I informed you when last we met, Strathmazeran presents several features of interest upon which I asked the Trustees' advice, and it seems to me that if we proceed with the work we shall be in a very favourable position indeed.

Grants and loans are based upon the total cost of a hall, including materials, labour, and architect's fees. When the labour is voluntary, as we hope it may be to a great extent in Strath-mazeran, the grant is still based on what the hall would have cost if the labour had been hired. In the event of all the constructional work being done voluntarily, the cost of material is taken as three-fifths, and of labour as two-fifths, of the total cost, excluding architect's fees. Thus, if our material cost us, say, £330, and we did all the building ourselves, the grant and loan would be made on £550. In effect, we could expect a grant of £183-6-8 and a loan of up to £183-6-8—actually more than our total requirements. The loan would naturally have to be guaranteed, and, as you will observe, the Carnegie Trustees prefer that a community should furnish several small, rather than one or two large, guarantors.

Further, we could expect grant and loan in similar proportions on our architect's fees, or what these fees would have been if our architect had made his due charge. Now, Mr Thompson, one of the shooting tenants at Cairnbeg, who is himself an architect, has interested himself in our project, and most generously offers, through Miss Margaret Davidson, to draw up a plan for us free and without charge—providing an example to all of us which I am sure Strathmazeran will appreciate and follow.

Thus, Mr Mackie, I feel that matters are sufficiently advanced to let us call that general meeting we discussed, and I am sure you will agree that you, rather than I, a new-comer, should convene the meeting. I imagine that a notice in the P.O. or shop window and at the church door will suffice for the general public, but it would unquestionably be advantageous if we secured the interest of our leading men in the Strath by sending them a personal letter of invitation. Mr Thompson must certainly be invited specifically.

May I suggest that your notice be general, merely stating the place, time, and purpose of the meeting; but that your letters provide an agenda, which might run:—

a. Need of Village Hall. *b.* Uses to which it can be put. *c.* Help to be expected from Carnegie Trustees. *d.* Situation and obtaining of feu. *e.* Design and material of construction. *f.* Cost and finance.

You may prefer to put these matters less formally, but it is essential that we begin our work in the most strictly business-like way. For example, our agenda ought to be circulated at the public meeting—or written up on the blackboard, since I imagine the school is where we shall meet. For the same reason, our men of consequence in the glen should meet with yourself and myself prior to the public meeting in order to beat out a programme of work, decide upon the committees we shall want, and generally prepare to give the public all they must know in a straightforward, cogent, and time-saving fashion.

Your acquaintance from Banffshire who is taking Croft Roy sounds as if he should be a tower of strength, though, of course, one must be careful not to antagonise the other native crofters by showing any tendency to defer to his judgment rather than to theirs. It will be interesting to see what he makes of Croft Roy. It is most indiscreet of me to confess that I would like well to see good, fresh, energetic east-coast blood coming into these charming but rather relaxing Highlands. Please never divulge that I said so, or one east coaster will find himself sent packing.

Yours very sincerely,

GEORGE LOCKHART.

3

Mrs Alice Lockhart to Mrs Maisie Dalgarno,
Edinburgh

MY DEAR MAISIE,

Here we are, almost through November. I can hardly believe that this month, to which I was looking forward with some dread, is nearly over. Oh, yes, the weather was just as dark and wet as I'd expected, but somehow we didn't notice it, because we are living what Janet's favourite novelists might call in capital letters a FULL LIFE! Do you know we are out three nights in five? I hasten to put your mind at rest, though. It's not cocktail-parties we're attending, but committee meetings, and I bet no cocktail-party was ever as entertaining as committee (pronounced with the 'o' long and the accent on the last syllable) meetings are in this Highland glen. Picture us, clad in waterproofs and wellingtons and armed with flash-lights, plowtering down the road and revolving mighty schemes in our minds as we jump the puddles!

The reason for all this is that Strathmazeran, egged on by George and Adam Mackie, the schoolmaster, has determined to build a village hall. I shan't bother you with all the secret visits and diplomatic letters that have passed between the schoolhouse, the manse, and the Carnegie Trustees. But I must tell of the delicious public meeting that was held in the school.

George and Mackie, the sly villains, had previously inveigled the leading citizens of the glen into a pre-meeting. They even tried to induce Mr Thompson, an architect who was shooting at Cairnbeg and very generously offered to make a plan for the hall and give his advice free, to come from Aberdeen to this pre-discussion. By the way, it doesn't sound a very Aberdonian trick to offer skilled services free, does it? But I'm discovering that I'd a wrong idea of Aberdeen altogether. I thought the people there all spoke Broad Scots—like the B.B.C., you know —wore hodden grey, and were *grippy*, to say the least of it. Well, Mr Thompson proves himself very far from grippy, and as for the other things, a young lady came to visit him from Aberdeen who was a perfect vision. And her accent might have come straight from—well, from a Michael Arlen novel. So now we know better.

George and the schoolmaster and the leading lights managed to get everything pretty well cut-and-dried at their pre-meeting, and I gather that the proceedings were quite amicable until Baron Alexander Cameron blew in in a frightful hurry and announced that he couldn't wait a moment, but he thought Strathmazeran should buy an army hut, which was cheap, and good enough. Sinclair, his favourite enemy—though not his only one by any manner of means—

immediately rushed in to say that public money shouldn't be wasted on cheap trash; and there was the dignity of the hall. He made a longish nasty speech at dear Alexander, but that worthy rather turned the tables by walking out in the middle of it. George was very put about. Really, I wish our good and godly elders would take the principles of Christianity home to their bosoms a bit more than they do.

However, the little meeting got everything cleared up, and its members came to the general meeting all full of nice business-like proposals and thinking they'd get the affairs of the hall settled in ten minutes. They had another think coming pretty soon, as Janet says. If they imagined they could rush Strathmazeran, they were sadly mistaken. Everyone at that blessed general meeting was out for the evening's entertainment, and they weren't going to have the fun cut short just for the sake of cut-and-dried plans, not they!

Davidson, Cairnbeg, was in the chair, and called on Mr Mackie to explain things to the assembly. Mackie was cogent, and really, if his teaching is like his behaviour that night, he must be a grand teacher. He wrote the agenda on the blackboard, and then he wrote all his points there too. The trouble is that the audience didn't want to be instructed or to listen. It wanted to talk. I could plainly see it was growing restive under his logic, and when one or two interrupters, pretending to be seeking the elucidation of something Mackie had said, were brought summarily back to relevant issues, you could feel the people were unhappy. Immediately Mackie finished, the entrancing Shamus Munro leapt up to orate. He told us how good it would be to have a hall, and what we could do with it. Then, if you please, while thanking the absent Mr Thompson fulsomely for offering his services—Shamus demanded we should give the poor fellow a hearty cheer, and believe me or not, we did it!—while thanking Mr Thompson, Shamus offered to design the hall himself. It was to be built in sections in his backyard, and then dragged to its final resting-place and chained to the mountain-side. It was to be mounted on an axis and moved round every time the wind changed. He added that he'd often built houses like that in California, where they have earthquakes. Mackie remarked very tartly, 'There are no earthquakes in Strathmazeran.' Shamus fixed him with a dreamy blue eye and said, 'No, but there are cows.' Shamus looks rather like the prophet Elijah in one of those illustrated Bibles. He hasn't got the beard, of course, but has the same benign expression and subtly superior bearing, as of one who holds intimate converse with the Eternal.

Eventually the meeting did what George and Mackie wanted and agreed to all they'd determined on. Then came the sparkling bit of the evening, when the office-bearers were elected. George is treasurer and Mackie secretary, but there are *dozens* of committees. Strathmazeran has nothing to learn from anyone about the workings of democracy. Every time the meeting was in doubt what to do next it elected another sub-committee. Here as elsewhere people are touchy, too, but our brilliant Highlanders have hit on a scheme which goes far to mollify everyone's feelings. Every single person of adult years and moderately responsible character in the glen was elected to a committee. As there are General, Executive, Working, Advisory, Finance, Entertainment, Teas, and Labour committees, as well as others I can't recall for the moment, you'll see it's not too difficult to share out the honours of office. Mrs Mackie and I are joint conveners of the Concert Committee, in view of the fact that she once took part in amateur theatricals and I've been playing the organ on Sundays because our organist has gone to have her tonsils out. Now that I've become a sort of impresario in Strathmazeran, Janet and I have been digging out my old music and the drawing-room ballads of our youth. I thought that we ought to concentrate on Gaelic songs, but my bold Highlanders think they're old-fashioned and want something modern! When they said 'modern' my heart sank, because I envisaged hot jazz, and I didn't think I could manage that. However, what they mean is Scots or English songs, instead of Gaelic ones. English is still in Strathmazeran a new tongue. The Highlanders have an even greater sense of history than their brother Lowland Scots. You can picture me, then, teaching that old and trusty friend 'The Bells of Saint Mary's' to the glen's angry man, Alistair og Maclagan. Mrs Mackie is having what she calls 'a sair fecht' choosing a little play for her part of the work. The worst of most eligible one-acters is that they're written in Broad Scots or Cockney, both equally unsuitable for Highland voices to pronounce.

Dear me, in reading over what I've said I find I haven't explained that the function of the Concert Committee is to run a concert to raise funds to help build the hall. And the same for the Entertainments Committee. Then the Teas Committee will provide cups of tea and sandwiches for the men who, under the direction of the Labour Committee, will build the hall by voluntary labour—one of George's dearest schemes, and I think his most foolish. It would be far easier to raise all the money to build the hall than to keep our gentle Highlanders at it when fishing days come.

Having, like a true wife, got in the bit which George has been impressing on me is most important, I mustn't forget to tell you that Margaret Davidson is running the Dance Committee. When this committee was mentioned Wullock Mitchell, our rapscallion beadle, insisted that it should be called 'The Dence an' Swuss Drive Committee.' It took me quite a while to realise that Wullock's 'Swuss Drive' was a whist-drive. At first I thought it was some foreign exotic hitherto unknown to me.

I am glad to say my guild is going on well. I don't suppose I could lure you up to talk to them on Women's Foreign Mission work in India? I do so want my wifies to see that there is a world beyond Strathmazeran. Now I must really be done. Janet (who, by the way, is on the Teas Committee) is waiting sternly for me to send an order by Peter the vanman to our butcher. We are getting very adept at shopping in the wilds. With much love from your old friend

ALICE.

4

*Rose Sinclair, Shirramore, to
Archie Cameron, Kerrow*

. . . and when the hall's built it'll be so much easier for us to meet. It's terribly difficult just now. I've been worried these past few days in case Dad had been hearing gossip; several times I've caught him looking at me in a queer, *suspicious* way. So, Archie, the hall has *got* to be built, so that we'll have badminton and concerts and choir-meetings to take us out in the evenings. You and I must urge our stern fathers on to get *our* hall up . . .

Archie Cameron to Rose Sinclair

. . . but somebody had to stay at home if the old man went to the meeting, and that's how I missed your note. However, as soon as I got it I tackled him. He came home from this meeting which was held prior to the general meeting looking as pleased as punch, by which I knew he'd been up to mischief, and it wasn't long till he told me how he countered your father and advised the minister and the dominie to build according to Strathmazeran's purse, which was very shallow, by erecting an army hut.

When your note came I got on to him and said how delighted all his enemies would be to see him living up to his stingy reputation. Well, that did it. First of all I got the devil of a dressing-down, and then he despatched me with orders to do about ten different things at once, which is his way when he's rattled. I'm perfectly certain that as soon as he was rid of me he wrote to the Hall Committee saying that his suggestion of an army hut was not meant to be taken seriously. But we shall see what we shall see. All the same, Rose, we can't go on for ever like this. I'm not going to have you worrying in case some Paul Pry sees us and tells your father. Won't you let me tell them all, as I long to do, that I love you and we are getting married? And if they don't like it—oh Rose, I hate hiding what I'm proud of, I hate acting as if we were doing something to be ashamed of. It's not right of us. However wrongheaded our parents are, we oughtn't to deceive them . . .

6

Alexander Cameron, Kerrow, to
Rev. George Lockhart

DEAR MR LOCKHART,

I have decided that it would be a great pity to mar the beauty of this glen, and endanger our prospects of obtaining a generous grant from the Carnegie Trustees, by concentrating on cheapness. In fact, it would be a mistake to purchase an old army-type hut for a village hall. Strathmazeran has its honour to uphold amongst the villages of the Highlands, and we must not be outdone in the quality of our hall.

I should be glad to discuss with you whether the sum mentioned at the general meeting as a price for the hall takes account of this. £600, was it not? Too cheap!

Pray ignore the question of guaranteeing the Carnegie loan—should we need it. I shall deal with that matter.

Yours sincerely,
ALEXANDER CAMERON.

7

Adam Mackie to The Carnegie United Kingdom Trustees

DEAR SIRS,

At a public meeting held here on Tuesday, November 17th, it was decided to build a hall in this village, provided a feu, and your assistance, can be obtained.

I was appointed secretary of the general committee, with instructions to get in touch with you. (I am schoolmaster here.) In order to save your time, and my own, I enclose a copy of the minutes of the meeting, from which you will see that Strathmazeran, though the village itself is small, contains a fairly large population. I attach a one-inch map of the district, with farms, crofting townships, &c., ringed in red, and figures denoting their respective populations inscribed within each circle.

The total population of the district served by the village of Strathmazeran is 258, a number which is swelled in summer and autumn by summer visitors, fishers living at the hotel, shooting tenants and their staffs.

The projected hall will be used to stage a variety of entertainments, including dances, concerts, plays, ceilidhs, whist-drives, and badminton. Besides these entertainments we propose to have a Young Men's Club, for which I am making myself responsible; a W.R.I. branch, to be initiated by the wife of a large sheep-farmer; Boy Scouts, for which our clergyman and myself will be jointly responsible; a choir, organised and trained by Mrs Lockhart, the wife of our minister, who is herself a fine musician. We shall naturally use the hall for public meetings of various sorts, which are at present held most uncomfortably in one of my schoolrooms.

We lack the activities I have described, not because the people do not want them, and not because the leaders of the people are not prepared to take the initiative in organising them, but because we have no meeting-place. If you provide us with help I assure you that the hall will be made very full use of.

We already have promises of guarantees far beyond any loan that we are likely to ask, or you to make.

I send by separate package the suggested plan for the hall. Our proposal, as the plan makes clear, is that the walls be built of railway sleepers spiked to a cement foundation, strapped on the outside with wood straps—or harled if funds permit—and lined inside with celotex, or canvas or thick brown paper oil-painted; the roof to be asbestos sheet.

I shall be glad to learn whether the design of the hall, and the materials we desire to use, meet with your approval.

Yours faithfully,

ADAM MACKIE.

8

*The Same to The National Council of Social
Service, London*

SIRS,

I have received your letter which purports to be a reply to my letter of November 19th to the Carnegie United Kingdom Trustees. I am at a loss to understand why my application to the Carnegie Trustees, a Scottish body, domiciled in Scotland, deriving its funds from a Scotsman's benefactions, should be dealt with from London, and why London should be thought better acquainted with Scottish conditions than are the people of Scotland itself. Had I known of this arrangement I should have explained matters more fully in my earlier letters to the Carnegie Trustees.

The sleepers we propose to use are five inches thick; the weatherboarding you advocate is one inch thick. We have been promised sleepers by the railway officials at a keener rate per lineal foot than any at which we can buy weatherboarding.

Your comments on the lay-out of the hall we wish to build in Strathmazeran do not take into account Highland weather conditions. If we put the main entrance at one end of the hall and the cloak-rooms at the other, then everyone must arrive in time for a function—so easy for people who have to travel several miles on paths and bad roads!—or else late-comers must walk the whole length of the hall to get rid of their wet coats. Or sit in them. During a dance late-comers must march across the dance floor in their sopping boots and coats.

We designed our hall with cloak-rooms at the entry end to avoid these unpleasant things. We made the cloak-rooms open from the hall, instead of from the porch, to avoid all risk of pilfering; and also (but you may not comprehend this) to discourage the men from hanging their coats at the back of the entry door and running out and in from the hall to get at their half-bottles.

However, since these are your objections, and you control the grants and loans, we had better rule your assistance out of our plans and proceed with our alternative scheme to buy an army hut at our own sole expense.

I am,
Yours faithfully,
ADAM MACKIE.

9

The Same to the Same

DEAR SIRS,

I am very glad that you have decided to pass our plans. We shall certainly make a changing-room for players in any plays we may present, and situate it at the far end of the hall from the entrance, behind the stage and alongside our kitchen.

Our architect informs me that the boards which you object to at the gables of the hall are beams triangulating the gables above the sleepers, and are thus essential to the construction.

I shall lay your approval, and suggestions, before my committee and acquaint you with our progress as soon as possible.

                    I am,
                              Yours faithfully,
                                        ADAM MACKIE.

                         10

                 The Same to the Same

DEAR MR ——

We have obtained a feu and can now proceed—amicably, I am sure! Having struck a blow for freedom, and Scotland's right to self-determination, may I thank you for your courtesy, and the equanimity which you preserved so well under my attack. But I am sure you have had long and sore training in patience. Thanking you again,

Yours sincerely,

ADAM MACKIE.

Alistair Og Maclagan to Adam Mackie

Mister Mackie. You are a big one now, secretary. Ha, ha. Mind you yourself. Pride. Comes before a fall. There is some in the glen is saying. Why was not I sent a letter about the hall? Oh but we're not big ones. No money, No good. A notice in the shop is plenty. I was here let me tell you and my folk before me when there was no sheep farmers thought of. And will be again, The day is coming. We will have a good treasurer anyhow. Rev. Mr Lockhart you can trust. Who will do your work, building, volunteer labour, that is what I am asking. Mebbe you will write a public notice. Aberdonians coming in will do it, Mebbe. My boy's sums was right, answers is what counts, not how it's done, method. Mebbe I will write a notice soon. Education

79

Committees, that is what they are for, keeping an eye on the likes of you. They will like to hear.

ALISTAIR MACLAGAN.

12

Rev. George Lockhart to Adam Mackie

DEAR MR MACKIE,

I return Alistair's gem. If I were you I would not worry. You certainly could not have written a letter of invitation to him without sending one to every man in the parish, and to expect you to do that would be even more of an imposition than we have already put on you. I suppose Alistair really could do us harm, but I would not let him worry you. If I were you I'd send him a kind note—it might even be mildly flattering—and if that doesn't work let me know and I shall deal with him. I have handled more difficult parishioners, and even angrier men, than Alistair before now.

No, I don't think your dealings with the Carnegie people were in the least high-handed. In any case, they were successful, and I have learned sufficient Jesuitry in my life to let that be a justification.

I understand that your Banffshire acquaintance arrives at the term, the 28th. I shall make a point of calling on him at an early date.

Yours sincerely,

GEORGE LOCKHART.

13

Adam Mackie to Alistair Og Maclagan

MY DEAR ALISTAIR,

I was overjoyed to get your letter, and I have given the points you raise the most serious consideration. Why not come down some night and bring Mrs Maclagan with you so that we can discuss the Hall together? In a matter of this sort all people with any influence must get together, and one can put a great deal more through hand at an informal meeting than in public debate.

May I say that it is men like you who belong to the glen and know its people that we depend on to get things done. There is this dance, for

instance. We simply can't get along with it
unless we have you with us.

Yours sincerely,

ADAM MACKIE.

14

Alistair Og Maclagan to Shamus Munro

Shamus. Come up quick. There is this dance
coming. It is put on me to do it. It will be
a great affair, I can tell you. We will make
a big thing of it, you and me. You will electrify
the loft, Kerrow. There is lots to do, food,
baking, ornamentations. I am trusting you. Do
not fail.

ALISTAIR.

DECEMBER

I

*From Rose Sinclair, Shirramore, to
Archie Cameron, Kerrow*

ARCHIE DEAR,

You know I can't possibly go to the concert
or the dance at Kerrow. Goodness, my father
would take a fit. Perhaps we shan't see each
other till Christmas is past, so I'm sending you
wishes for a merry Christmas just in case—and
love—or is that shameless of me even at this
season?

Dad is watching me. He looks suspicious and,
do you know, I'm blushing just as if he could
see what I was writing.

ROSE.

2

Archie Cameron to Rose Sinclair

DEAREST ROSE,

If there was a little more peace and good-will
on this particular bit of earth there'd be no

need to wish me a happy Christmas. I'd be seeing you, and then I'd be as happy as a king. But, Rose, you surely don't want to see me when you write saying we'll maybe not meet till after Christmas? Rose, even if you can't come to the dance—don't you want to see me?

ARCHIE.

3

Rose Sinclair to Archie Cameron

MY DEAR,

It was you who said we couldn't go on meeting by stealth, deceiving our parents. And if we tell them, they won't let us meet. I was only respecting your scruples when I said we mightn't meet until after Christmas . . .

4

The Same to the Same

Archie, you're being unreasonable and cruel. You know I want to see you. I long to see you every day and every hour. This awful quarrel is as hard on me as on you. Perhaps it's harder on me. Oh, Archie, don't let's quarrel now of all times! Even if we don't see each other we can think of each other—as I do, but I can't bear to think of you angry with me. Please, please, Archie.

ROSE.

5

Archie Sinclair to Rose Cameron

MY DEAR,

I'm a brute, I'm a beast—oh, it's this letter-writing. And not meeting. Did I have scruples? That must have been long ago. I've forgotten them—won't you forget too, and forgive me, and maybe meet me, just for a little while—to-morrow? We'll arrange to have a little while to ourselves, if it's only an hour, on Christmas day.

ARCHIE.

6

Rose Sinclair to Archie Cameron

Oh, Archie, to think of you forgetting your scruples! All right, and maybe you'll not scold

85

me this time if I wish you a Happy Christmas
and a *Better* New Year.

ROSE.

7

*Charles Watt, Croft Roy, Strathmazeran, to his wife,
Mrs Madge Watt, Mill of Hackerton, Rothiemay*

DEAR WIFE,

This is to say am safe arrived and settling
down fine in the Hielands. The weather is very
wet. It is just as well you didn't come, for
things on the place are a fair mess, the house
not too good, etc. You will be comfortable
where you are and not bothered with the rheumatics as you would be here. The house is
that damp you cannot put on your socks in
the morning on't airing them. So I am glad
you are in safe quarters, though missing you
and the bairns. I will take back all I ever did
say about liking to bothy it again. You spoiled
me for it, Madge. I do not fancy brose the way
I used to.

Now, you will be saying you know that fine
without me telling you. So here goes for a bit
of gossip, which is more than you let on I ever

give you. Well, Madge, they are a great lot
here. I have not said much yet to any of them.
Least said soonest made up for is what I think.
But it is not ill to hold your tongue here, for
all the folk is wanting to speak and not listen.
They have a great gift of the gab, Hielanders,
but are not great doers so far as I see, though
I am not on for condemning them till I've seen
more of them. All the same, I do not think
they are great ones to act. Take this place,
Madge—it is a nice bit of land, good land, forty
acres arable I make it, and four hundred hill,
though the advertisement to let said fifty and
three hundred. But that is Hielanders all over,
always taking a bit off or putting a bit on for
no cause at all. I could tell you things they told
me that if you believed them would make your
hair stand on end. There is an ass of a chap,
Shamus they call him, which is James likely,
Shamus Munro, that makes himself out a dealer
and engineer and what not. Well, he has a
tongue that would make eagles out of white
Wyandottes. He told me he was bad with a
cold last week and took an aspirin afore he went
to bed and in the middle of the night when he
wakened the bed was floating on his sweat and

the steam pouring through the thatch of his roof. Also he had a bad eye and took it to the doctor, and the doctor took it out to clean it and laid it on a plate. Then Shamus and him turned their backs a minute, but chanced to look round just in time to stop the doctor's cat making a pounce on the eye. Did you ever hear the like! I told him I wondered at him, a grown man, putting such lies out, and I was not interested in a threshing-mill, especially from a man that would tell lies as easy as spit. He was none put out.

To return, the place is nice, facing the sun, good soil though dirty and in bad heart. The rent is not big, and we will soon make a differ in things, but it will be dour going. All the same it will be worth it, for the place is as good as our own, this being a croft according to the Act, so that you can't ever be put out but it's yours even on. That is a thing which strikes me as queer. The crofters here have sure tenure, which many a one that we know would give his right hand for. But will they do anything for their own good? Not them; they just let it slide and blame the landlord. They were telling me he would not do anything, building houses and that. Well, Madge, you know I have no law for lairds, but that put my back up and I said to them: 'Why don't you do improvements your nain selves? You'd never get your rent put up for them, as I've had, nor lose a place you slaved to make, as I did.' Oh, they didn't like it, they were taken aback, I can tell you, but I was never one to think one thing and say another, as you know.

There is room for pushing folk here, Madge. Take the house here—no water, not in the house or the steading or the fields either. Fifteen pounds I make it, not counting labour, would put the water in. Fences and dikes terrible, gates out of the ends of beds. That's not the thing, it looks bad, a body can't have his self-respect when he lets things go. No garden at all, not a spade's been turned here since the place started. Windows I would not put in a henhouse. Gravel on paths? Well, I wouldn't like to say so much as the things I've seen would be worth calling paths, just ruts.

Now, Madge, do not be getting frightened and thinking you are coming to a terrible place, for it will be different before you come. You know me, I like things nice. Forbye that, if the folk here make a living you and me will do well. I marked out a nice bit for the garden, and where the hens will be is sheltered with a bonny birch wood. I sent to the Department for a copy of this new housing Bill. We will see what it will do. The steading is fair to middling good, better than the house. I was near shifting out of the house with my bed. There is a good dry loft.

Who do you think I met here but Arch Mackie's loon, you mind him, wee Adam? What do you think, he's the dominie here and liking it well. He is very snug with a nice wife and two lassies. Some folk say 'It's a small world,' but what I say is 'It's a big world and full of Aberdonians.' I was real glad to fall in with him and have a crack. It was nice hearing a kent tongue again, for they have a strange twang here, I can scarce make them out. Mr Mackie told me there was a great ploy going on in the glen with a hall to be built and he said he would like fine if I helped him, which I will do as soon as I can see a bit in front of me. I will not say more of that at the moment.

I took a wee dander down to the pub yesterday night—Madge, you're thinking wrong. I have other roads for my pennies than down my throat, so do not worry—ever now. The pub is a canty bit place, but very through other, which I think is the way Hielanders like things. There is no organising ability in them, is my view. Anyhow, me and the publican fell into a blether about this and that, price of beasts and so forth. He is a nice-spoken fellow. I think he does not so bad. Says I to him, it'll be mostly summer trade you depend on here, tourists and fishers and that. Oh yes, says he. Says I, you'll have a bit of ground. Oh no! But, says I, it will not make a great differ any road, milk and butter and eggs and fruit and honey and vegetables will be that easy and cheap to get from the crofts.

Madge, when I said that he laughed. He did, he laughed like to burst, and what do you think? All the hens and eggs he buys comes from Jock Shewan up at Delnies at the back of Rothiemay! Can you beat that? I says to him, would you be better suited with local stuff got near hand? Yes, of course, he told me. Vegetables and fruit. There's no use speaking of it, they're unobtainable, says he.

I did not say more on the subject at that time, but Madge, here's where you and me come in. We will make a deal, I'm fair certain. I think his money will be good all right. But I am not going further with it till I hear from you. There is many a fair tongue speaks out of a toom pocket. Do you take a turn round by Delnies, and when you see Jock Shewan make on you're needing day-old chicks, and come at it on the side where they're for, Strath-mazeran. That will likely set him off saying he does dealings with folk here, so you will say you heard they were awful bad payers in the Highlands, and if he does not think that, we will know it is all right. Ach, hear at me telling you the road to go at him! You will know yourself how to hear if the pub is good for its money and pays quick.

I will have a place for the hens afore the New Year. I was telling the folk here that I was counting on our hens to lay right off. When I told the folk that, they went on something terrible, just as if it was not right for hens to be laying at this time. Likely it will be against the rules.

I am longing till I can say for you to come,

as I would do if the house was not so damp.
But I will keep on big fires, though it is gey
dreich sitting afore them all by mysel'. If I take
a thought and run up to see you about the New
Year you will not be surprised. There is that
pest of a Shamus bawling at the door again,
so no more now. Give a kiss to Ella for your
affect. husband,

CHAY.

8

The Same to the Same

Was that lonely thinking of you all, Madge,
especially yourself, not forgetting the wee ones,
I took it in my head for certain I will run down
for the New Year. I will turn up, so do not
be expecting me at any fixed time. We were
always althegither at New Year, Madge, since
long past now. The folk are nice enough, kind
you would say, telling me not to be lonesome
but to drop in, especially at this time. But
other folk's fires are not like a man's own. I
am staying quiet in the house here over the
Christmas, thinking of you and wishing you all
the best, but I will not go out visiting though

they are prigging with me. It will be weari-
some waiting, but all the nicer when it's New
Year and I see you and tell you the news. Now
no more, but I will see you and let you have
the news by word of mouth, and I am sending
a bittie paper to put something special in the
bairnies' stockings seeing I am not with them.
You are not needing me to give you the wishes
of the season, for I am aye wishing you guid
days and lang.

CHAY.

9

Shamus Munro, Knockbuie, to Mrs Macaskill,
the Post-Office

Woman, do not bother me with your mangles.
Mangles! what sort of thing is mangles for
a man like me to be taking notice of at this
moment when all is depending on me, and folk
are busy thinking we will soon have concert
and dance if Shamus and Alistair is left alone.
Think shame on yourself! There is a time
for mangles and a time for bigger importances
which you should heed and do not send messages. I will not come down. I will write if

I like, I will write saying No Mangles! Me is it you are saying is frightened to look you in the face? Me that showed the power of the human eye against many wild beasts heretofore, especially lions, tigers, wolves, ect! This is no way to be going on. I will be doing what is best for all so now No More Mangle. I am surprised at you coming between Strathmazeran and the Hall I will build beautiful. I will sort your old mangle time enough. So no more or it will be very bad between us, look you after Post Office and leave men to big works,

SHAMUS.

P.S.—You should buy a little Ringer like I told you. I have agencies, cheap. I will make a special price seeing it is you. You can easy afford Ringers, coining money out of P.O. We will be seeing your name high up on lists of subscribers for Hall. I will tell you what to give.

P.P.S.—Do not be trying to put me off, wishing me Merry Christmases. I am not holding with Christmas. It is Pagan. The minister will tell you. New Year is different. So do not try saying Merry Christmas at me and Mangle in the same mouthful for I am seeing what you are at with your tricks, woman. Peace and good-will should be on the earth and NO MANGLES.

IO

Adam Mackie, Schoolhouse, to John Thompson, Aberdeen

DEAR MR THOMPSON,

Our public meeting to discuss the building of a hall in Strathmazeran went off very well indeed. Everyone was almost embarrassingly enthusiastic (as well they might be, when you, a stranger to the Strath, provided them with such a gener-ous example by designing a hall and offering your advice free). Your prompting also enabled me to bring the Carnegie Trustees to see reason, and, in short, we are ready to begin. We have the feu, promises of guarantees against any loan we may raise, and popular enthusiasm behind us—for so long as it may last. I am sure you will have heard all this already from our minister, Mr Lockhart, who was instructed at the meeting to write to you conveying the community's appreciation of your exceeding kindness.

It is delightful news that you are coming to

96

visit Strathmazeran at the New Year and, against my own personal hopes, I trust you may have snow and stormy weather during your stay so that the hinds will come down from the hill-tops and afford you good sport. I shall be home in Aberdeenshire at New Year, but when I return on the 4th I shall look forward to seeing you, and you may even delight my wife and myself by visiting us on the 5th and helping us to celebrate Aul' Eel.

We hold the first function in our drive to raise money for the hall on Christmas Eve. It is to be a Concert and Dance, and the arrangements are in the astonishingly energetic hands of your own old ghillie, Alistair Maclagan, who is very tyrannical about the business and resents any interference. But I have dared so far as to suggest meekly to him that you be sent an invitation. Perhaps you might be willing to say a few words during the concert regarding the construction of the hall?

If we do not meet until after New Year may I wish you a very happy Christmas and good sport.

Yours sincerely,
ADAM MACKIE.

*Margaret Davidson, Cairnbeg, Strathmazeran, to
Mrs Armstrong, Edinburgh*

DEAR MRS ARMSTRONG,

It was very kind of you to write us all such
nice letters and we are very glad that you were
so happy with us. Indeed it was a great pleasure
to have you here. Thank you, too, for the huge
parcel of crinkled paper and the decorations you
sent for the dance here. They'll make all the
difference to the granary loft where it's to be
held. We can't help laughing over the dance
programmes, though. You see, Alistair Og and
Shamus and myself could not agree about them.
Alistair is all for what he calls 'heavy' dances—
'with a *swyte* in them'—and Shamus was on
for terrible foreign things nobody in Strathmazeran or anywhere else ever heard of, and I
wanted a few of what the Strath calls 'soft
dances,' foxtrots and onesteps and waltzes. I
never dreamed Alistair would run away and
draw up a programme of his own and send
it to you and ask you to have it printed and
decorated. He came in with your works of

art yesterday and to hear him you'd have thought he'd drawn the designs and done the printing himself. You never let on to us that you were such an artist! Of course, now, seeing the programmes are so beautiful, we have put them up in the barn, and Alistair is licking his lips with pleasure at having got his own way against Shamus and myself. But you will see him yourself when you come up for our great affair. Yes, the 24th is the date. We are expecting Mr Thompson from Aberdeen as well. He is coming for the hind-stalking for a few days, so we're looking forward to a fine cheery houseful over Christmas. Strathmazeran appreciates your coming such a distance to the dance very much indeed.

Our arrangements, for a wonder, are fairly well advanced. Mrs Lockhart and Mrs Mackie are doing the concert part, but along with Shamus and Alistair I have the business of arranging the loft and seeing to the tea and the dance. I'd made up my mind to have it in the Kerrow granary, but I didn't exactly know how to make sure of its being there without offending Shirramore, who, as you know, is at daggers drawn with Cameron, Kerrow. However, as good luck would have it, Sinclair from Shirramore came down one day to see Dad, and who should appear later but Alexander Cameron? My, thon man thinks he's Archie! Well, of course, when Cameron came in the door Sinclair was for off, but I caught his waterproof tails and said, 'We must decide whether the dance is to be at Kerrow or Shirramore.' 'Shirramore naturally,' said Sinclair. 'We have more space at Kerrow,' said Cameron. But though they glowered at each other like two wild beasts I just got out a pack of cards and said 'We'll cut for it.' Cameron cut low, so I said 'Kerrow.' But I didn't tell them whether the high card won or lost before they started, so if Cameron cut high, it would still have been Kerrow. Men are such sillies with their quarrelling, and for all their airs and graces they're easy to manage—well, some of them. Dad is very cute.

I will say for King Cameron that he has gentlemanly ways, and though it meant a lot of work and bother for him, clearing the loft, he was extra nice about it and ordered his men to help us all they could. He made a stage for us (he said strangers would be coming, and we must let them see that Strathmazeran knew how to do things; the man's full of *bigsiness*, but this time it's for a good cause, so we'll forgive him). And he helped us to make a little kitchen and promised us the loan of a new oil-cooker for the tea. I'm not sure, mind you, that he wasn't anxious to show the rest of us what a grand kitchen he keeps at Kerrow.

Shamus and Alistair said they would instal electric light if we would promise them car batteries. The worst of Shamus is that you just can't disbelieve *everything* that comes out of his mouth, and like a fool I trusted him to do the business right. In the end Alistair had to go and ask Mr Mackie the schoolmaster about it. Alistair is very thick with Mackie now, in spite of all he used to say about him. It turned out that Shamus had the wiring all wrong, but it didn't take Mackie long to put it right, and now Shamus is going about the glen laying off about the great electrical undertakings he's had to do with in foreign parts. It's a good thing he's doing that now because when his bulbs wouldn't light he went down to poor Nell Macaskill the Shop and interfered with everything and wanted to cut bits out of the telephone wiring, and she was in such a state she kept the mail-van waiting an hour for the mail-bag two days in succession. For all that, she has a soft spot for Shamus, and though whiles she miscalls him, I wouldn't like to say anything against him to her.

Now that the lights are working there's a great load off my mind. With your grand decorations and programmes, and the ever-greens and holly from Shirramore and the manse, the loft is going to look byordinary grand. Mrs Urquhart the Hotel is giving us crockery and things like that as well as sandwiches, and Janet the Manse is baking and will help with the teas and washing-up. But then, everybody is baking, so there should be plenty to eat. We are getting the Inverartney band, and though they offered to come free we're to pay them. I know those bands. They just go off and get drunk and play when and what they like unless you pay them properly and have a hold over them.

Now, this is all my news. Dad is just come in to say that he'll be at Inverartney station meeting you at the 5.15 on the 23rd. Mother says to tell you how she longs to see you and have a right good ceilidh with you and Mr Armstrong. I hope you'll both be in good form for Alistair's square dances. It's the only sort of hard work he ever does. You'll need to be doing your Keep Fit exercises to get into condition for Quadrilles followed by Lancers! No more now. Every kind wish from all at Cairnbeg,

yours affectionately,

MARGARET.

12

Mrs Lockhart, The Manse, Strathmazeran, to Mrs Maisie Dalgarno, Edinburgh

MY DEAR MAISIE,

So many thanks for your princely gifts to us. It was sweet of you to send the album of music too, because it's not only a great pleasure in itself, but it'll be such a help in getting up concerts for our hall. As for the cake and the currant-bun and the shortbread—I feel we can withstand a siege with them in our cupboard. We had rather a business getting our own Christmas shopping done here. However, I got George to take Janet and me to Inverartney and we managed away wonderfully. We made a lot of plum-puddings in November, and they came in very handy for presents for the folk here, who, though they love dumplings, don't like the fash of making them.

We have just emerged battered but victorious from our first grand concert and dance for Strathmazeran's new hall. It took place on Christmas Eve, and I'm afraid I wasn't feeling quite so full of peace and good-will as I ought to have been. You see, Mrs Mackie the Schoolhouse and myself were ordered to run the concert part of it, and now that it's over I wonder how C. B. Cochran keeps his sanity. The fact that he does just shows that putting on a slick London production is easier than running a Christmas concert in Strathmazeran.

Our first task was to gather folk who would be willing to perform. You've no idea how difficult this is in a place where there is no communal activity at all. As a stranger, too, I was dependent on a good deal of hearsay, which of course turned out to be all wrong. However, I got George to run me about—mercifully it's been a fine open winter so far and the roads are nice and clear—and I managed to unearth quite a few performers. Others I tackled after church, much to Janet's disapproval. Then Mrs Mackie sent word round by the school-children, and finally we left messages at the post-office and the hotel. So what with one S O S and another we had a fair number of embryo stars waiting us at the schoolroom on a bonny frosty winter night. Mrs Mackie and I had drafted out a provisional programme that afternoon over tea and mince-pies, but, my dear, our noble Highlanders would have none of it. I'd been given hints before that they didn't want old-fashioned songs (by which they mean Gaelic songs) but modern ones, which to them are English or Scots songs. In spite of this I put in two Gaelic items in my list. The cast explained sweetly but firmly that it was only when 'veesitors' were there that they sang in Gaelic, but when they were by themselves they preferred songs in English. However, when it came to choosing songs in English not one single person could as much as tell me the name of a song. Luckily I had brought an old Students' Song Book with me, and I tried out a few things for them on the piano. You know what school pianos are —or you can guess what like they are, any-way—and then it was too shadowy to see the music, so I had to vamp like anything. Rapturous applause greeted my efforts, but as I wasn't there for applause but to choose songs it was rather annoying. As long as I played I had flattering attention. The instant I tried to come to business the audience fell blandly but inexorably silent. If the dominie hadn't appeared I'd have been sitting there yet. With his help we got songs and singers fitted together, and he actually wrote a little play specially for the folk here, who speak book English and so can't attempt a dialect play or sketch. Most one-acters seem to be in dialect.

I'll pass over the nightmares of rehearsals when either nobody turned up or everybody came late and wanted to gossip instead of sing. The dominie certainly had the best of it, because he got up some carols with the children and of course had them under his thumb all day. As time wore on, more and more messages kept coming in to the kitchen telling of yet another and another who was to sing. Shamus was responsible for this. He can't sing a note himself, but, being all overcome by the spirit of helpfulness, he set forth to Inverartney per his tricycle (yes, that's his vehicle) and he rounded up a whole gang of singists. George kept exhorting me not to worry, but it was easy for him to be saintlike when all he had to do was to cut armfuls of holly for Margaret Davidson, who was doing the hall decorations. *He* didn't have to fret over nasty details like getting our own piano up to Kerrow and providing tea for Shamus's concert troupe after they arrived by bus from Inverartney. I tried to scold Shamus about his singers, but he turned a melting and proud smile on me and said, 'Yes, they are lovely singers, and look at all the folk they will bring with them for the dance and all. And it's the Christmas besides.'

Well, the great night arrived, and Christmas Eve at that. I shan't ever forget it, and Kerrow Concert will be found graven on my heart when I die. Although the affair wasn't billed till half-past seven at night, Janet and I were up before it was daylight (not that that's so very early these winter mornings). We packed hampers and hampers of foodstuffs, and I was so wrought up I nearly packed our own turkey as well. The reason for all the food was that tea had to be served twice at the affair. This is a dreadful country for giving meals to travellers. The fact is, everyone lives so far from everyone else that tea is really necessary to succour one's visitors, though I wasn't prepared to find that tea had to be served after the concert and then in the middle of the dance. Thank goodness we hadn't anything to do with the kitchen end of the business, as Margaret Davidson was in charge of that. Actually, she told me, most of the kitchen work was done by the Kerrow maids; but an urn had to be kept hot all night in the barn and tables laid out with cups and plates and eatables. We'd hardly done packing the last scone when Alistair Maclagan and Wullackie Mitchell came with the hotel lorry for the piano, and Alistair seized the opportunity to practise his song for the evening. It was, alas, our ancient friend 'The Bells of Saint Mary's,' and you should have heard Alistair exhorting 'the young loves and true loves' in a thin, high, somewhat inaccurate tenor. Wullackie and Janet then, if you please, saw fit to practise *their* duet. Yes, they volunteered off their own bat to do it, and they chose 'The Crooked Bawbee'! Really, I think Janet's mind is going. What worried me was that even at that moment I didn't possess a full programme of the items for the concert. You see, Shamus's Inverartney contingent had gaily promised to sing, but hadn't vouchsafed to say what songs they'd chosen! And I was accompanist.

Then I was anxious for these wretched Strollers to come in good time, because I had volunteered to give them tea in the manse before going up to Kerrow. And we had to be up at Kerrow early because the electricians had been promised our car battery for the footlights. Well, of course the Inverartney troubadours were late, so late in fact that we had to leave without them and send Shamus down to our kitchen to await them and direct them on to Kerrow. And still I hadn't any idea of their songs.

King Cameron, as the Strath calls him, was chairman of the affair, and I rather dreaded telling him of this stupid predicament, but, after all, he knows his fellow-countrymen and wasn't the least put out. At first I thought we weren't going to have any audience at all, but at eight o'clock a great crowd of people erupted into the hall, and for the next half-hour more and more ancient motor-car engines conked out in the steading. By the time the concert was over we were crowded out. We didn't wait for everyone to arrive, but started in a little after eight, only thirty-five minutes late. For the first half everything went off swimmingly—at least I'm told so, but I was so upset at the non-appearance of our visiting performers that I couldn't really tell how the items looked or sounded. It wasn't till the middle of 'The Crooked Bawbee' that Shamus appeared at the head of his gang. Janet and Wullackie screeched their loudest to drown their tread as they marched up the barn, but all in vain. They tramped up to Cameron and gave him the list of their songs—no music, mark you. I keeked round the piano and Cameron handed the slip up to me. My dear, there were six singers and all of them except the last two had chosen songs we'd already sung. I felt quite unable to cope with this, so we just gaily repeated the programme, and if I'd ever had any doubt of Strathmazeran's manners this laid them for ever at rest. The audience sat courteously through 'Scotland Yet,' 'Bonny Strathyre,' and 'My Nannie's Awa'' as if they'd never heard them in their lives before, and applauded enthusiastically. Then a saintly looking ancient with a bald head and a long brown beard carefully trimmed off into two points, appeared on the platform and wheezed into my ear that he didn't want the piano but would I 'chust give heem a not'? I did so, and after several false starts he burst into a Gaelic song, the words of which I supposed he was reading out of the book he held at arm's length. After the second verse he stopped and remarked severely to the audience, 'The lights is that bad here I cannot see, man.' He scrabbled about in his pockets and produced a pair of specs, and still he couldn't see. Then he discovered that he'd been holding the book upside down! I gave him another 'not' and away he flew, and this time he sang dozens and dozens of verses in the most woeful voice. About verse forty-five he stopped for breath and Cameron led terrific applause. The mannie, who, I discovered later, is called The Shenler (a Gaelic corruption of General), was frightfully angry, because he hadn't half finished his song, but as the applause continued he walked off the platform in a huff and wasn't seen again for hours.

Well, you'd have thought that would have been enough excitement for any poor Lowlander, but worse was still to come. The last singer, a Captain MacDermott, got up to sing 'Scots Wha Hae.' I thought thankfully that it was at least a change—and short. MacDermott made a very picturesque figure indeed, for he was tremendously tall, very thin, with a red face and enormous white eyebrows, and he was clad in all the glories of kilt and plaid. He even had a sword, on which he leant as he sang. It all looked very rugged and grand, but as he warmed up to the song he began to stride up and down the stage brandishing his weapon. I had to cower over the keyboard to avoid having my ear cut off, and the poor wretches in the front row thought their last hour had come, and Mrs Macaskill actually crouched on the floor as the excited man swooped and swished his claymore round their heads. George said that even Cameron blenched.

The Armstrongs had come up from Edinburgh for the occasion, and Anne told me afterwards she wouldn't have missed it for worlds. Well, perhaps—but I can tell you I'm not going to endanger my neck again, and I'm going to keep a very firm hand on any other concert there may be here. After the first tea was over Mackie dismantled the footlights and got our battery back into the car and we went home. We didn't stay for the dance, which was, I believe, a frightful success, though the lights gave out because, of course, half the batteries weren't properly charged. Efficiency, thy name is not Highland. Poor Mackie is very bitter about the batteries going phut and wants the blood of their owners, but after all everybody is saying what a grand affair it all was, so I don't think he should worry further over it. The playlet he wrote was thoroughly successful, and half the glen is quoting bits from it already. Now, this had better be the end. I've been writing before the study fire, and it's nearly midnight and the fire is out. Many thanks again, and all good wishes for the New Year from Strathmazeran and your affectionate friend

ALICE.

13

John Thompson, Cairnbeg, to Miss Aileen Leask,
Aberdeen

DEAR AILEEN,

Arrived safely and am very busy planning what to do if snow comes, bringing the hinds down. At present the weather is mild and deer are high up, too far out to be gone after in these short days. But there are white hares, and rabbits —and festivities.

Everyone here is very well and asking for you. There are great goings on with the new hall, and I am the Strath's darling. Really, you'd think I'd designed a palace. I'm not happy, though, about Mr Lockhart's plan to build it by voluntary labour. It would be all right if there was one tradesman, or even handyman, amongst them, but the best they've got is Shamus—and the worst? well, you saw their home-made sheds and henhouses and gates yourself.

We had the Grand Concert and Dance in Kerrow granary. Margaret Davidson ran the dance, very well, too, in spite of her dreadful helpers, Shamus Munro and my old ghillie, Alistair Og Maclagan, who has suddenly mellowed, and forgot to scowl when he told me he was *almost* well. The dance was a most jolly affair. I danced with everyone and came home at four-thirty on Christmas morning dead beat. You women are wonderful. Margaret was dancing or serving teas all night (and she's a fine dancer, as light as a feather), and came home with me looking as fresh and pretty as if she was just going out for the evening instead of coming home from a barn dance. No more now. I hope you have a good time in London. Love from

JOHNNY.

14

Robert Sinclair, Shirramore, to
Alexander Cameron, Kerrow

SIR,

I have poinded ten ewes marked A.C. on left horn, no ear mark, keeled red on right shoulder, very thin, which I understand by these signs are your beasts. My shepherd would have put his dogs on these ewes and driven them back where they came from, though that is a constant work because of the state of your fences (also the ewes are so thin they would get through netting wire). But they were weak, and he was frightened they would die on him if he chased them.

It is natural for hungered sheep to try to get out of their starvation into good pasture, but I shall be obliged if you take steps to check your sheep's coming into my ground, either by feeding them better or mending your fences. Otherwise I shall be forced to take an action for damages against you, which might very well go hard with you, especially if the Cruelty Inspector heard of the case. I shall also be obliged if you send your shepherd forthwith to collect the ewes I have poinded. I would prefer that he brought cash to pay their dues rather than your cheque. It will be better if you send him quickly, as I do not want to be forced to charge you beyond your means.

May I add that I do not want to see sheep belonging to you, four-legged *or two-legged*, within my land.

I am, yours faithfully,

ROBERT SINCLAIR.

15

Alexander Cameron to Robert Sinclair

MY DEAR SINCLAIR,

I enclose cash herewith in settlement of your claim for keeping my ewes, and I am delighted to have the opportunity to help you with your rent. Say no more about not paying by cheque. I quite understand how difficult it is to retain money paid by cheque when the bank is clamouring for an overdraft to be reduced. I have instructed my lawyer that you are broadcasting it through the glen that my sheep are starved, and I await with interest his advice upon the slander, which I intend to rebut and seek redress for by every means in my power.

I shall inform you of the further steps I take in this matter. With best wishes for Christmas and New Year,

yours sincerely,

ALEX. CAMERON.

16

Robert Sinclair to his lawyer, George Walsh,
Inverartney

DEAR MR WALSH,

A neighbour's sheep are trespassing constantly on my land and causing trouble and disturbance. I shall be glad to have your advice on this and another small matter concerning the same man and hope to call on you on Thursday of this week.

Yours truly,

ROBERT SINCLAIR.

JANUARY

1

Alistair Og Maclagan to Robert Urquhart,
Hotel-keeper

MISTER URQUHART,

The whisky I got New Year was BAD. I am
not right yet. It might have been the death
of me so take note it was dear enough.

ALISTAIR MACLAGAN.

2

Mrs Maclagan to Finlayson & Co.,
Chemists, Inverartney

(*Telegram*)

Send immediately seidlitz powders aspirin
epsom salts.

MACLAGAN,
Strathmazeran.

118

Archie Cameron, Kerrow, to Rose Sinclair,
Shirramore

HONEY,

Things are becoming quite impossible, and I'm just about at the end of my tether. Rose darling, it's all very well to say 'Have patience,' but all patience will get us is old age, for our dear parents, instead of growing wiser and becoming friendly, are acting more foolishly every day. Did you know that your father is taking an action for damages against mine because of our sheep straying into your ground? And my father is going to sue yours for slander because he said we starve our sheep. My sweet, if we don't say straight out now that we love each other and are going to marry each other in spite of everything, there will never be another chance, for the bad blood between our fathers won't vanish, it'll increase. If we don't make up our minds to brave their anger now, then we'll just go on meeting in secret like guilty conspirators till we're old—or found out. And that'll be worse than speaking out.

As it is, your father is suspicious, and so is mine. Rose, why should we hide what's a thing to be proud of, not ashamed of? It's our fathers who are doing wrong, not we. I can't go on like this; I hate deceit, and it *is* deceit . . . Oh my! and this is how I wish you a good New Year! . . .

4

The Same to the Same

It's too late, Rose. The fat's in the fire now. Our parents had a public set-to in Inverartney Auction Mart and had to be restrained from fighting. Did you ever hear the like? It would be comic if it wasn't tragic for us. But what's worse than their making public objects of themselves, they dragged us into it—yes, they discussed you and me at the pitch of their voices in one of the most sharp-eared and malicious-tongued places in all the country, Rose! I'm not going to go into what was said. Kind friends will bring it to you soon enough, for the country's ringing with it. You see now that our fathers love their spite against each other more than they care for us. Oh, they're not so scrupulous about our feelings as we are about theirs, I can assure you! Well, when my father came home he turned on me like a raging lion. Likely he forgot I was his son, after all, and had his own dislike of being shouted at. Did I know that people were coupling my name with yours? I said No, I did not know it, but if they were, I was proud of it, and I wanted to marry you and would marry you if you'd have me, and what was he going to do about it? I must say for my father that he has always respected things I showed I'd made my mind up to have. When I asked what he was going to do to stop us he said he didn't need to bother, your father would do that. Then he got angry again and threatened to dispossess me. Maybe it's fortunate I have the money mother left me. She knew him of old. His threat made me really angry. All the resentment that's been gathering against our parents' arrogance and malice broke loose, and I said straight out if he preferred to keep his enemy and lose his son, the world was wide, and you and I weren't going to let our lives be poisoned for ever by silly rancour and jealousy. I am going down to see your father as soon as I hear from you. I love you, and the whole world can go to pot for all I care so long as I have you.

Archie.

5

The Same to the Same

Oh, Rose, when Jimmy brought your note and I read it I thought I'd die. Rose, you can't mean it. It'll anger your father for a little while, and hurt his pride, and my father's pride as well. After all, I also am the only child he has, and he's old too. They'll be angry and hurt for a little while, but this between us is for ever, and if we kill it, there'll be something in us dead for ever. My dear, we can't go on meeting now. Every eye in the glen will be on the watch for us, every gossip waiting to run with tales; and don't you think it'll hurt our fathers more to get stories at second-hand, and to think we're deceiving them? They'll think it anyway, even if we never met, and I couldn't go on living here and not seeing you.

At any rate, if these accursed lawsuits go on I'm going away. I'd be a witness, Rose; I'd have to tell the truth; your father *did* slander mine, and my father's sheep *are* straying on your ground.

I love you, and I'm not going to lose you like this just to save two angry foolish old men's pride. I'm going down to see your father face to face. Then, if it's no good and his pride means more to you than I do—Rose, I can't write it, I daren't think it. We're at the parting of the ways; it's now or never, happiness or—I couldn't stay in this country even if—Oh, I can't say it. I put it out of my mind that I may lose you, because it's very near.

ARCHIE.

6

Roderick Maclean, Craggan, to
Charles Watt, Croft Roy

DEAR MISTER WATT,

Excuse my writing, but Allan Macgregor, Knock of Clune, was telling me of conversations he had with you in which you described

Smallholders' Co-operative Societies in Aberdeenshire where you come from. Am deeply interested in same. There is a crying need of such in these parts. Prices especially coal are cruel and a Co-operative would do well, every crofter would join. I am sure. Perhaps if you were finding time to spare, drop in for a crack. We hold by the old thing, Old New Year. We would like to be giving a toast to your success and many days among us and all the best in the year to come. We might get a few of us together. I can tell you names, some maybe would best stop out. There are bad payers in the world. Hoping we may see Mrs Watt amongst us soon,

yours truly,

RODERICK MACLEAN.

P.S.—They are telling me you have hens laying in winter where you come from. Do not count on that here. The weather is bad here, and very wet. If a man kept count, hens do not pay, but the women will have them.

P.P.S.—Thinking it over, I will take the liberty of coming in to-morrow and we will discuss Co-operatives which I am interested in for good of community. I would like to speak about fences, gates, etc. also. Sheep get free run of crofts in winter, it is the custom. Some were saying you should not mend fences, gates, etc. at this time owing to sheep being in habit of going through same at certain places. I will put you right on all these matters. It is different from Aberdeenshire I am sure.

7

Charles Watt, Croft Roy, to Shamus Munro

MISTER MUNRO,

Take note of this and let there be an end, for I am sick tired of you and your plans and your engines and your lies. I do not want a threshing-mill and if I did I would seek it from a man that was a millwright and sound in his head. I do not have any scrap-iron and I will not lend you money, take shares in your business as you call it, to help you to buy scrap-iron, and I am not interested in the Government wanting you to help them with Rearmament, gathering old iron for them. My hens do not clock in the middle of winter and I will not give you twopence for your home-made contraptions of brooders made out of old oil-tins and I do not care where the oil-tins came from. I would not trust you to sell day-old chicks though I had millions of them. I am telling you the plain truth, Mister. I am sick tired of your nonsense, and if you put your nose among my concerns further I will set my dog on you and that will start you off nice and quick in the New Year you are speaking such a lot about.

CHARLES WATT.

8

Shamus Munro to Charles Watt

DEAR MISTER WATT,

I have nice dictionaries full of correct spell-ings, also dog-biscuits will make dogs bark, growl, ect. very fierce even though poor trash and no heart in them. I could be giving you as much biscuits as would give your dog a right meal and I would not make a charge because I am wishing the poor brute a nice start for his New Year too.

SHAMUS MUNRO.

9

John Thompson, Cairnbeg, to Miss Aileen Leask,
in London

MY DEAR,

I do think you are being unreasonable, unless
you want to quarrel with me, which is poor
fun really, because I simply can't hit back. I
wrote you a short letter because there's so little
here you're interested in. If I told you about
my stalking you'd be bored. You told me
you were bored to death when I wrote you
from here in the autumn with news of our
shooting. You've no interest in the people
here or in their goings-on. But as for their
being yokels and my preferring to associate
with them rather than with you and with people
of my own class, whatever that may be—darling,
it's not true, and you know it's not true and
you shouldn't say it—unless you want to hurt
me. Sometimes I think you do. Well, I'm
poor spiritless game, Aileen. It hurts me terribly
to hear you say such things. My friends here
—yes, I am happy and proud to call them my
friends—the Davidsons and all the rest, even to

Alistair Maclagan himself, are real gentlefolk, whom I like and sincerely respect. And as for quarrelling with me because I mentioned Margaret Davidson—heavens, Aileen, what's wrong in that? If I found fault with you every time you told me about the men you know and I don't (this Arthur Cotton you met in London, for example) we'd be like cat and dog. Oh, don't let's start nagging and casting up to each other at this of all seasons, please!

We've had some snow, and I was out in Corrievreac yesterday and got two hinds after a lovely stalk, belly-deep in drifts of snow. It was quite deep up there, and the sun shone and you saw nothing but white hills against the blue sky, with Strathmazeran and its woods and farms and houses far below. A stalker has a fine life, better than designing council houses. Oh, it's so free! You really feel the old year is done, gone, blown and washed away, and a new one's begun, all white and shining. (Well, blazing would be a better word for Alistair Og's New Year.)

I knocked one hind over when she was going full gallop, and we dragged the two beasts home over the snow just as night was coming on,

with Merry Dancers flashing in the sky. I never
saw anything like it. But this'll bore you, so
no more of it. My dearest, good-night, and if
I annoyed you, forgive me. In a few days,
when you come back from London, we'll speak
seriously about our own affairs, when we'll be
married, and where we'll go for a honeymoon,
and how we'll furnish our house and everything. I have a hundred plans I'm dying to tell
you. Good-night. I'm waiting till I see you to
wish you happiness and everything this bonny
New Year.

JOHNNY.

10

The Same to the Same

Aileen, you don't mean this! What has happened? What have I done wrong to make
you change your mind all of a sudden? I've
been half-distracted since your letter came.
There's some miserable mix-up. I am coming
home at once. When we meet and speak you'll
tell me what's wrong—is it because I didn't go to
London with you? But you didn't ask me. I
didn't think you wanted me. I'd have gone—

I'd go anywhere—do anything—Oh, what's the use of writing! We always misunderstand each other when we write. Tell me when you're coming home, what train you're coming with. You can't mean what you said! You promised; everyone knows we're to get married. Please, *please* write and say it's a stupid mistake.

JOHNNY.

II

The Same to Mrs Aileen Cotton, London

(*Telegram*)

Wire received. Sorry cannot meet you Aberdeen. Staying here few days. Hope you will be happy.

THOMPSON.

12

Rev. George Lockhart to Andrew Duncan, Edinburgh

MY DEAR FRIEND,

A thousand good wishes for the coming year. May all your enterprises be blessed with happiness. We are both getting on in years, Andrew, and New Year marks another stage on our soon-to-end journey, but still I love it and still it fills me with hopeful expectations. Many, many thanks for your welcome letter and the magnificent parcel with all its seasonable gifts. My wife is writing to you herself to express her gratitude, but I must thank you also for everything, and especially for the books, which I have devoured. Books are truly a godsend on these long, dark winter evenings, though I should not like you to imagine that we are wearying, or lack occupation in Strathmazeran. Far from it; time goes past on the wings of the wind, and there are a hundred things to do which make each new day a pleasure to look forward to. I will confess that when I left Edinburgh, though I was immeasurably relieved to be free of the arduous labours of a city charge, which were beyond my strength, yet I had forebodings lest we, and in particular my wife, should find life in this remote Highland glen quiet and dull. There was also a fear in my mind that the people might not take us to themselves. We are, when all is said and done, foreigners, Lowlanders in a strange country. Ah, it is anything but dull in Strathmazeran, and the people are hospitality itself. At this

present moment our glen—already I call it 'ours'
—is enlivened by something I could well spare,
but which seems to pervade the whole world,
country and city alike, and that is Strife. There
has been for many years a bitter quarrel between
my leading elders, and their antagonism has
suddenly been fanned to flame by untoward
circumstances. Matters have gone so far as
threats of litigation, and you know what evil
and unforgettable results follow in the train of
lawsuits which are actuated by personal animus.
I have taken both men seriously to task, as was
indeed no more than my bounden duty. I
pointed out to them that their position as Chris-
tians and leaders in the congregation imposed
an obligation to show an example to my flock.
Alas, the human heart is a wayward, obdurate
thing, in Strathmazeran as elsewhere. My elders,
I doubt, turn a deaf ear to all except the prompt-
ings of their pride. It is a great grief to me,
the more especially since I have heard it said,
with what truth I know not, that the son and
daughter of these two men are enamoured of
each other. I sorely fear that their parents'
enmity may poison the children's lives.

That, I say, is an excitement I could well

spare. And, of course, at this juncture of the year ministers are always busy with funerals, for now the old, of whom there are many in Strathmazeran, feel their strength fail. Already I have lost several of my parishioners whom I had learned to cherish even in the brief time I have known them.

But enough, my dear Andrew, of my worries, with which I ought not to burden you at this of all seasons. I was overjoyed to hear your news of Sandy's continued success. The boy will go far. I am confident both of his abilities and of his capacity to direct them rightly. He has character and brains. Without the one, what avails the other? We are at a stage in the world's history, the world's grim history, when character in our young men is precious as never before. They have it in their hands to mould man's future to anarchy or order. I pray that it be in peace. But how easy it is to find fault with others, and especially with rulers of nations, when quarrels arise. I of all men should know better, who cannot even reconcile his ruling elders. But I shall try my utmost, depend on that!

Well, as I was saying when I harked back

to my troublesome elders, we have found winter in Strathmazeran gayer and busier than I ever dreamed possible. To begin with, the weather has been open, and considerably milder than it used to be in Edinburgh. Then we are constantly visiting, or being visited by, my really charming congregation. And, of course, we have our new hall to build, with all the meetings, entertainments, and negotiations that implies. We have begun to collect from door to door for it, and also to circularise our land-owners and shooting tenants, who are already responding in the most generous fashion, to such an extent, indeed, that we have almost a hundred pounds banked from subscriptions alone. Over and above that, we made thirty-five pounds at a concert and dance we held at Christmas time —an eminently successful function which drew people from far and near to the granary loft at Kerrow farm. My wife busied herself with some small matters connected with the concert, and enjoyed the work immensely.

Now, it is a strange coincidence that along with your letter I should have received a note from the newest of my parishioners, an Aberdeenshire man called Watt who has come to farm a croft here, a very solid, sensible shrewd man in my first judgment, and one to depend on. Watt, like yourself, is worried over our decision to build the hall by voluntary labour. He says—I have his letter beside me as I write—and excellently he does write, every letter perfectly shaped, copperplate such as I think we shall never see again—well, as I began to tell you, Watt says: 'Voluntary labour is all right as long as nothing else is doing. As soon as other work starts, lambing, road-making, ploughing, turnips, all will leave hall, maybe in bad weather with roof half on. Better to collect more cash and get hall built by contract. You can't count on volunteers. If all work, good and well. If one starts dodging, everybody says "Look at So and So," and they stop too. Voluntary work goes as quick as the slowest. Also, there is need of bosses, and in voluntary work all are bosses.'

Need I say that your own warning, to similar effect, weighs very strongly with me, and I was deeply perturbed to receive two such minatory communications as your own and Watt's on the same day. But I still feel that both yourself and he are unaware of the generous spirit of mutual helpfulness which prevails amongst the people here, and which will, in my opinion, carry us through every stage of our task triumphantly. My heart is set on doing this thing. The people are willing, are eager, and only require leadership, which I shall gladly give. As a concession to you, dear friend, I intend to propose that we employ one or two skilled tradesmen to direct and control our volunteers. We shall see. I have sounded a great many of my congregation and they do not share your own and Watt's and—alas!—my wife's doubts.

Now I must draw to a close. With renewed thanks for your gifts,

Your affectionate friend,

GEORGE LOCKHART.

13

The Same to Charles Watt

DEAR MR WATT,

I thank you for your second communication re village hall. Yes, I see your point when you say that if we employ and pay one or two skilled tradesmen, then our voluntary workers will tend to feel that they also ought to be paid.

I myself scarcely think that this feeling will arise, because the tradesmen will come from outside the glen, and will therefore derive no further benefit than their employment from the hall, whereas our local workers will have the use of it to look forward to. But, in any event, I think we are safe to leave this difficulty out of our minds until it arises. May I wish your wife and children the happy and prosperous New Year I have already wished you. We look forward to having them among us.

Yours v. sincerely
GEORGE LOCKHART.

14

Miss Janet Colthart, The Manse, to her sister
Mrs Katherine Hamilton, Peebles

MY DEAR SISTER,

I am glad you got the things you needed with the money I sent. I thought it would be better to send you the money as it is very difficult shopping here unless off catalogues and by post and that is a thing I never did believe in though the folk here are terrible catalogue-shoppers and not good catalogues at that. Just cheapjacks. Thank you very much for the gifts you sent, and it was real nice of wee Jimmy to send me the kettle-holder he made. I've got it hanging by the mantelpiece, though it's too bonny to use.

Now for my news. We spent a very quiet Christmas here, as the folk do not hold with keeping it but observe the New Year instead. It is at least one sign of sense. The mistress of course got a lot of parcels and cards and had a great time herself getting her own parcels off. She went to the wee town, Inverartney, for her shopping. But Christmas Day passed off just like a Sunday only there was no church. I must say I was terrible surprised that there was no affair for the children, party or tree, but it seems that, though they have a treat every year and it's called the Christmas Tree, it never takes place till January. So when the schoolmaster came back they had their tree and a wee party in the schoolhouse. I went down to help with the tea. Mercy me, Katie, they are no organisers here but just plowter along in a steer. You should have seen the soss they were in in the wee anteroom, trying to make tea in a place no bigger than a rabbit-hutch.

I am not an interferer by nature, but if I hadn't taken charge nobody would have gotten a drop of real hot tea that night. But do you think they were grateful? Not them, they would rather no tea than being organised.

There was quite a party at Mrs Maclagan's on Hogmanay, tho' just as throughother as all the affairs here are. But she's a right genuine soul, Mrs Maclagan, and was fair beside herself when I brought down a wheen things for her bairns that I knitted myself. She asked Mrs Macaskill, Shamus Munro, Willie Mitchell, and some others, and me. What a grand supper she gave us, too! I'm not saying that easy-osy's my way, but now and then there's something to be said for it. After the supper was over we had songs and recitations and me and Willie Mitchell sang the duet we gave at the concert I told you about. Willie hasn't a bad voice though he's gey queer-looking in his person. Mrs Macaskill gave a recitation in Gaelic. Yon's a terrible language, Katie, you would need your tongue jointed in the middle and a bellows in your nose to speak it. That goat of a man Shamus came away with a great story of foreign parts and what he was doing to help the government with rearmament by collecting scrap-iron which is his latest scheme, and he finished up by asking us all to keep any old pots or aluminium hot-water bottles we might have. Poor Mrs Macaskill was near greeting by the time he had finished his lay-off about Mussolini and Hitler and the shells we would need to make out of our hot-water bottles. He has an utterance and no mistake. Then after a few more songs Alistair Og Maclagan turns on the wireless to get the midnight chimes and he stood holding his watch ready. Well, Katie, you'll hardly believe this, but when Big Ben rang Alistair bawls out in a great rage, 'You're fast, you fool of a Sassenach!' And nobody was allowed to say 'A Guid New Year' till it was twelve o'clock by Maclagan's time, which was seven minutes late. That's Strathmazeran all over. It'll be late for the Day of Judgment.

Well, after that all the men went outside the door and shot off guns and then we all got a drink, port for the ladies and whisky for the men. Just as genteel as at home I'm glad to say. Then we all went home. At least, I went home and the others went first-footing all the glen. Willie Mitchell got that drunk that his mother had to sit on him to keep him down. She weighs eighteen stone and still she could hardly hold him. I'm quite disgusted with him. And more than that, he wasn't fit for his duties as beadle last Sunday and I did the church myself. It's the first time for many a long year that the place got a thorough. You would have thought the master would have been angry with Willie, but no! He just smiled when I told him, and he even goes to call on Willie as if he was a real invalid and not a drunken disgrace. Mr Lockhart is a very saint-like man but is far too gentle with folk. Of course what he says is, there is plenty anger in the glen without him starting in to row Mitchell for what he calls his *frailties*. It's true enough, for his two head elders are making a fair world's wonder of themselves what with threatening lawsuits at one another and being near blind with fury that their bairns are seeking to get married.

I told you about Archie Cameron and Rose Sinclair if you'll remember. Some long-tongued gabbledygash went and told their parents just at the time there was a stramash (that's Gaelic for noise, Katie) between them anyway about sheep wandering between the two farms. All this happened about Christmas so I doubt there wasn't much peace and good-will at Kerrow and Shirramore. The two men met each other at the mart at Inverartney and had, I'm told, a terrible set-to, bawling at each other like bulls and going to take hands to one another. What an example for the rest of the glen is what I say. Now there's lawyers' letters bizzing back and fore even on. I'm right sorry for the bairns.

As sure as anything I never seem to get peace to write a letter to you, Kate. Here's Shamus Munro, I'm seeing him through the window and he's coming here. Drat him.

Later.

Well, Kate, that was Mister Munro complete with a split-new ridiculous scheme. He had the face to come in and ask for scrap-iron saying he'd mentioned it to me on Hogmanay. He even followed me into the scullery and went poking about amongst the mistress's new pans.

'What a boorach,' says he to me. I just told him there was no such word as boorach and would he kindly put down the steamer as he

wasn't going to get it. I was right sharp with
him and do you know what he said? 'Well,
woman, you don't require to make such a
machreach.' I'm sure I don't know where
he gets his words but I'm not going to let him
steal my pans, the dirty Highland trash. By
his way of it he was going to pay me for the
pans. Him and his helping the government
with their rearmament! I *boosed* him right out
the door as quick as I could and told him that
if there had been a few sensible women on the
government we wouldn't be in the state we are
now, digging holes in the earth for shelter as
if we were rabbits and sending folk like Shamus
Munro out for stuff to make guns and bombs.
Oh, he fairly climbed down after what I said,
and was as sweet-spoken as anything. So thinking I'd maybe been too sharp I gave him tea
and a scone. He tells me that the Burns night
is now to be shifted into February owing to
there having been a funeral last week. Apparently they just shift it about to suit themselves,
and Inverartney always holds it in September
when the visitors are north. I was fair affronted
at the liberty they take here, but Shamus isn't
easy put out and says he with his mouth full

of scone, 'Oh, Burns was a poet and poets never heed about exact dates. I'm a poet myself so I know.'

Now, I better close now, dear sister. Hoping you and James and the bairns are well.

Your affectionate sister,

JANET.

P.S.—That Shamus Munro has stolen the aluminium tea-pot. Wait till I get him!

15

Shamus Munro to The Editor, The Spectator

DEAR SIR,

I have observed from copy of your paper which came into my possession you have competitions, Limericks poetry. I am not interested in Limericks, there is no tune in them, but herewith poetry I wrote and very good, better than Limericks a long way.

> *Strathmazeran is a bonny glen*
> *Full of strong lads and lovely women.*
> *River called Mazeran runs right through*
> *And shortly we will have a good hall too.*

No man that ever saw this glen will say
There is better any other way
And I myself Shamus should know for sure
Because of all my great world tour
Wherein I wandered round the earth
Even as far as West Australia, Perth,
A nice city in a distant land
But not so nice as this glen where a happy
  band
Will soon put up a hall for dances whists
  eckcecker,
Than which there is nothing better.

                                    SHAMUS MUNRO.

P.S.—This will start off New Year fine in
your esteemed paper or I could make up extra
bit wishing you and many readers all the best.

16

The Same to the Same

DEAR SIRS,

Re your P.C. Do not send P.C.'s. Post Office
will be reading same, you should think of that.
How was I going to know your competition
finished last year, January? The date was torn

off your paper that I saw. Put date down middle
of page in future. Send back my poetry quick or
cheque, not crossed.

Yours truly,

SHAMUS MUNRO.

17

Shamus Munro to fourteen iron-founders and
scrap-merchants

DEAR SIRS,

Send me quotations, all sorts scrap lead, iron,
steel, aluminium, copper, tin, nickel F O B ect.
In big quantities which will help. God save
the King. This will be a good set-off for the
New Year for you. If your prices are right.

Yours truly,

SHAMUS MUNRO,
Engineer.

FEBRUARY

I

*Shamus Munro to The Minister for War,
London*

YOUR LORDSHIP,

Re your *speak* in the papers last week, saying we should get together and collect scrap-iron, I am starting off for to help you so do not fear, we will get shells made. I got a car which will be useful collecting all over Highlands, also trailer made to specifications according to my experience. I will let you know how I am getting on, so do not worry, folk are behind you, especially them that has seen the world and knows foreign parts like me. It is not nice to be under foreign power, niggers and that,

      your humble servant till death do us part,

                SHAMUS MUNRO,

                    Defence Officer.

2

Mrs Nell Macaskill, The Shop, to her cousin,
Elizabeth Macgregor, New Zealand

MY DEAR COUSIN LIZZIE,

It was awful nice of you to send me the card
and photo of yourself and your man and family.
Everybody here was very interested in it indeed
and was saying they would have known you
at once. Your man looks very well put on
and the bairns are real like him. You have
done well for yourself, Lizzie, and I doubt,
though you will be saying there's no place like
Strathmazeran, you won't be on for coming
back to it for a whiley anyway.

Well, here we are just in our usual, having
got over New Year fine though there's been
a lot of deaths in January amongst the folk
you know. Old John Roppie Macdonald at
the head of the glen (you mind he was in Croft
Beg, next your uncle Charlack's place) is away
and was buried a week past Friday. Then
Yalsach Maclennan (her father had the hotel
before the Urquharts) is off to the infirmary,
and they're telling me she's not like to see the

week out. Something in her insides. You'll be glad to know though that your old friend Allan Dure is still to the fore, though now retired from Croft Roy and living down in a fearful grand new council house in Inverartney. The house has a bathroom and all, and Allan says the bath's the handiest place for keeping salt venison in he ever had. There's an Aberdonian called Watt in Croft Roy now. He's not a bit like Allan, but very hard natured and keeps himself to himself. He was in here the other day and had a great machreach about my prices. I'm sure the carriage here is enough to double the price of everything, but he wouldn't hear that. I see he's been sending a letter to a big town store. Likely he'll be getting his things from them. Och well, I'm better without the likes of him, though I think that those that make their living in a place should buy their stuff there. His wife and family are coming here soon but I expect they will be as hard as himself.

You'll remember the Maclagans. Alistair Og you mind married Marsali Mackay one of the Torromans. Well, they had a new bairn in July. This makes the seventh. No falling birthrate amongst the Maclagans, but it's nice to see children about, especially since so many folk have left the glen. There's only twenty-eight scholars in the school now, and when you left here there were above seventy. Oh me, I doubt the old days are done! Still, the schoolmaster was saying if the Maclagans keep on he'll have to get another teacher.

Then there is Shamus Munro who was in school with us. He was in foreign parts for many years but is now home in the old place at Knockbuie. He's a great Shamus. Full of ideas for making his fortune. He was ever a one for schemes. And mind you, though there's many that make a mock of his notions there's a lot in what he says, and one of these days he will surprise them all. He comes here a lot but you needn't be thinking anything for there's nothing between us but friendship. He has a plan just now for gathering scrap-iron to help the government against our enemies. There's many never spares a thought to the government or that poor gentleman the Prime Minister who I'm sure can't help himself, him being English poor thing. Well, Shamus's idea is to gather all the old bits of iron lying about in the district and give them to the government to make bombs and that. He says they pay extra good prices and there's big fortunes being made out of helping the government in this way. It is interesting to me seeing that I am sort of in government employ myself, having the post-office I mean, and your money never comes to much just leaving it in the bank or post-office savings. Shamus says if you want to make money accumulate you must strike out and speculate. He is very clever at understanding things like that and explaining them. Anyhow I am glad it is government work he is on and not like last year, when he had a scheme for catching pike at Easter and selling them to the poor Catholics. Nasty smelly brutes, my wash-house was stinking with them after he hung them up waiting for to be taken to Inverartney.

We have a new minister here in place of the Rev. Macangus who passed away last year about this time. He is a very good man, name of Lockhart, but I doubt he was never at the college because I can understand every word he says on the Sabbath. He takes a great interest in the place, too, and is helping to get us a new hall in the Strath. Him and Mackie the school-master and Shamus are the heads of it. Mrs Lockhart his good lady is a real toff but with no side. She buys a lot from me and never says the price is too high, not that my price is beyond the thing, Lizzie, for I know as well as the next one that even toffs don't like being cheated. The Lockharts come from the south so have not the old language, but there's not many have that now even in the Highlands. I must not forget to tell you about the maid at the manse, name of Janet Colthart. She's from the Borders and is terrible bossy. Her way is the right way, and I'm thinking she has a notion of the men, too, and her well past forty. She is always running out to offer Willie Mitchell the beadle tea, and Shamus tells me he can hardly get away from her when he goes to give the Rev. Lockhart directions about the new hall. I could see for myself how she was on for the men on Hogmanay when we were at the Maclagans', but she's too fond of her own voice ever to catch a husband.

You were asking in your letter about the Camerons and the Sinclairs. I'm sorry to tell you that there is no improvement there at all.

In fact, things are very bad, and what makes it worse is that Rose Sinclair and Archie Cameron are going with each other and the fathers are just like to eat one another with rage over it. Jimmy Ishbel our postie carries the letters between Rose and Archie on the q.t. but he also carries letters from the P.O. to the fathers from lawyers in Inverartney. Of course, Lizzie, if it wasn't that you were in New Zealand and I can trust you not to pass it on I would never tell you this, or I would lose my job, but the lawyers' letters that are going are something scandalous. You always know them from the thick paper in the envelopes. There's talk of Cameron having Sinclair up for slander because he says that Sinclair said the Kerrow yowes were that thin they should be reported to the Cruelty. And Sinclair says that Cameron's yowes are forever wandering over his place and he's to have Kerrow up for damages. The glen has plenty to speak about what with the hall and the sheep-farmers not able to agree with each other. But it's not only in Strathmazeran there's rows. Young Mr Thompson, an Aberdeen architect who drew the plans for our hall, was one of the shooters at Cairnbeg last autumn and came back at New

Year for the hinds. Him and his young lady had a terrible cast out, with letters and wires going all the time. At last she wired from London she was getting married to some one else that very day. The poor chap got an awful blow, you could see it on his face when he came here to send another wire back. I was right pleased to see he wasn't going back to Aberdeen to meet her on her honeymoon—did you ever hear the like! the cheek of her to ask him!—but was staying here for a few more days. He helped them to mark out the place for the hall and Shamus and him worked out the measurements. He's away back to his home now, of course, and I think he was the better of the while he stayed on. I think he has a notion for Margaret Davidson though he doesn't know it himself. Anyway, he writes regular to her or her folk and it's always her writing that goes back. Time will tell, Lizzie.

I must draw to a close now with all good wishes for the New Year to self and family.

Your loving cousin,

NELL.

P.S.—It must be awful queer in New Zealand, having summer at the New Year, but I suppose that's just the modern way, nothing like what it used to be.

P.P.S.—I know it's late in the year to be wishing a Good New Year but this is the first letter I have written for this year so trust you will understand.

Nell.

3

*Charles Watt, Croft Roy, to his wife, Madge Watt,
Mill of Hackerton, Rothiemay*

Dear Wife,

This is to say all is ready and I am looking forward to Friday when you will come. I ordered hotel lorry for Friday to meet you. It is very unhandy here being so far from the railway. We will need a car or else motor-bike and sidecar. A little van or lorry would be very handy.

Now there is great goings-on with one thing and another here but I will not say much of them because it will be better speaking than writing. I will say the crofters here are very friendly, and one or two of them were at me to start a co-operative. But you know what that is, Madge, hard work and no thanks. I would not take on to be co-operative secretary for less than fifty pounds a year, and some of the men scarcely make as much as that out of their places in a whole year so they would be sweirt to pay me even if they were able. It would be hard-got money at that. You would need to watch out who you could trust. Very touchy they are here, full of pride, and not good at working together, as the minister will soon find out. He is planning to build the hall by ourselves, which is daft. I tried to say as much, but you know what it is when a man takes a notion in his head, he will not see reason. Mackie and me are taking it in hand quiet like to draw up time-tables for folk to work by. I will put myself down with horse and cart for a set-off and that will start everybody rushing in to go one better than me, seeing I am a stranger. They are easy to work on if you kittle up their pride.

Well, re co-operative, I took the chance to write the manager at the North-Eastern Co-operative in Aberdeen saying would they supply here. Yes. Then I wrote saying if I collected the orders and stood good for the cash, would the bonuses be credited to me? They said likely it would be all right if the orders came as from me and I guaranteed payment. They are giving 1/8 for feeding stuffs and 2/8 for seeds and manures on the pound for bonus. Also their prices are keen and folk here will do well dealing with them even if there's no bonus. I will need it all, with the risk and everything. I am told there are bad payers here. Glad to hear Hotel's money is good. When you wrote I went down immediate and tackled Urquhart who has the hotel, and he is keen to get his eggs and milk and cream local. I did not rush him, let him do the coming on is what I say, it will be better. We will need to have chickens fat for the autumn when the toffs are here, also plenty of eggs and cream and butter. Prices are big here as you will soon see when you come. The Shop is fair ridiculous. That Shamus does no good to it with his blethers; he is always there, hanging about. I am not bothered with him of late since I gave him a flea in his lug. I am hearing he has bought a car and is making a trailer for it to collect scrap-iron like the other tinkers. I am wondering where the money to do all this came out of. I have a good mind to take out what I put into the Post-Office Savings here.

The weather was very wild for a few days, but it is better now. They are telling me terrible things about the storms there used to be. Mebbe they're like the men that used to be, a terrible lot bigger and better than men ever was. See and put on plenty warm clothes and wrap the bairns up well. I am longing to see you, Madge. It is lonely kind here. A man gets accustomed to his own cheery fireside and takes ill with bothying it after a whiley. The bairns will be pleased to see their daddy again. They will be thinking he is off with the sodgers. Mr Mackie the Schoolhouse was sending you his regards and wants us down to see him after you come.

Love from your loving husband,

CHAY.

P.S.—That Shamus has gone off and I'm wondering what he's taken with him. Himself and Shop Wife put it out he was working for the government collecting scrap all round the place in the Hielands. He will get plenty bed-ends if they are not needing them for gates.

That is what they make their gates out of, Madge! Thon Shamus got a car, and he made a trailer, the hammering he had day and night you would think he was building a big ship and when all was done it was just a hurly he made. I am wondering where he got the money for a car. I do not like the look of him I can tell you. He will make gey little of it all, just for interest I got a firm to quote scrap-iron and then I heard what Shamus was saying in the way of prices. He is taking his prices out of the daily paper, for new manufactured iron. I said that to one or two and they told me Ca' canny with Shop Wife and not say a word against Shamus because she has a notion for him. We will not say many words to her anyway, her prices are some big for poor working folk like us, the toffs maybe can pay them.

Later.—It's lucky I did not close this, Madge, for just when I was thinking of going to the P.O. a storm came up again and terrible wild it is now, and the folk has just come for me to help them look for old Sinclair the sheep-farmer up at Shirramore. He went out after his sheep this morning and when he didn't come home his lassie got worried after a bit

so sent asking us to make a search for him.
Now I must off and help. I will tell you all
when you come. It is very wild indeed, so likely
all the folk say here about storms is not altogether lies. I am thinking the road to Inverartney will be blocked again, and so far as I
see there is no arrangement for opening it. If
it is open you will get this letter but if it is closed
I will wire. So if you get this letter just come
on as arranged unless I wire you to stay. I
will be sorry doing that for I am fair forfochened
with doing for myself in the bad weather.

CHAY.

4

Archie Cameron, Kerrow, to Rose Sinclair,
Shirramore

DEAR DARLING ROSE,

I faced up to my father, told him I loved
you and wanted to marry you, and was not
going to ruin our lives for the sake of his wicked
quarrel with your father. He raged and roared
a bit, and then he said, 'All right, Archie, if
you can get Robert Sinclair to agree to his

daughter's marrying you, I shan't stand in the way.' Alas, Rose, that wasn't really a surrender, because as soon as I mentioned the lawsuit, and asked was he dropping it, Dad just raised those eyebrows of his and looked insolent and said: 'Really, am I supposed to fall in love too? What has my lawsuit to do with you?' I said it was like to ruin all I hoped for, and if it went on it would drive me out of Strathmazeran. If he and your father went ahead with their litigation, and made their hatred of each other irrevocable by dragging it through the law-courts, then I must leave the place they were busy making hateful to me. I can tell you, Rose, I was wrought up and didn't mince matters, and my father saw I meant what I said. 'Leave it—alone?' he said. I told him Yes, if needs must. That staggered him. It staggered me worse than it did him. But oh, Rose, how could I live here and not see you, not speak to you even secretly, not have anything in the wide world to hope for!

I don't see why my father should be taken aback to discover that his son has a few of his own characteristics, but he was, and after he stared at me for a while he said in the angriest,

most hurt voice, 'All right, if Sinclair agrees
to this nonsense, which I don't for a moment
expect he will, I'll allow his slander on me to
pass.' It wasn't very graciously done, but still,
it was done. He'd promised; we'd got over
the first difficulty and we never expected to.
I could have leapt and sung for joy and I couldn't
keep the happiness out of my face, which probably hurt him worse than anything I could have
said. Isn't it funny that making me, his only
son, happy should hurt him? But dear Heavens,
it's time this awful folly ended, for their sakes
as well as ours.

I was busy thinking that now we were half-
way to overcoming our parents' objections,
when my father came back and glowered at
me with a very red face and bawled 'But don't
ask me to go kissing him.' Well, I just couldn't
help it, I burst out laughing at the awful picture
of Alexander Cameron and Robert Sinclair
solemnly kissing each other. I laughed, and he
glowered, and then he couldn't help it either
but had to grin, and he really isn't such a bad
old ruffian. The trouble with him is he always
has got his own way.

I haven't felt like laughing since. I'm so

terrified in case your father does what mine expects, which is to say No. He mustn't; we won't let him. I am writing to him, oh, very formally, to say I'd like to come down the day after to-morrow—I've got a job I must do to-morrow, and he'll be at the sale at Inverartney in any case. I'm saying I want to speak to him. I don't know how I'll get through the time between. If he says 'No, don't come,' of course I'm going just the same; I'm going to ask him to give us his blessing even if he puts the dogs on me. If we have children, Rose, I wonder will we be any wiser with them? I think it would have been different if our mothers had lived. They'd have put a stop to this daft feud. Women have too much sense to make a god of their pride. When we're married—och, my sweet, I've got to keep my courage up. If your father says No—then I'm going to you, Rose; you couldn't have two people in the same family both being cruel to me, could you? I'm going to say 'Rose, marry me, I've a little money, I can make more'— but he'll not say No. I have a feeling in my bones that he's getting as sick of the feud as we are, and as I'm sure my own father is.

Pray for your father to get a good price for anything he takes to the sale to-morrow—or that he'll buy all he wants dirt cheap. So that he'll be in a grand humour when I go down next day.

ARCHIE.

5

The Same to the Same

Oh, Rose, isn't it awful, this is the day I was going down to see your father, and he sent me quite a moderate little note to say he'd see me. And now this storm has come out of the blue. Couldn't it have waited another day, and me with my courage screwed to the sticking-point and my tongue all ready to be sweet as honey—such eloquence I've been practising, you'd never believe I had the words of pleading in my head! But then, clever as you are, gem amongst women, you don't really realise how I adore what I was going to plead for. And now there's a blizzard which I'm sure'll send your father out to the hill too, so that even if I did go down he wouldn't be there.

I'm scribbling this note and sending it with Jimmy the Post—you mayn't get it, though. If he manages to trauchle through to Shirramore, you'll know I'm out on the hill in a blizzard, for which I don't give a haet because I love you. We're getting ready to go after our sheep. I'm afraid we're going to lose a good many. Is it very wild with you? I never heard such wind as there is here. When you go out in it, you'd think the noise was hammering you; it's like being beaten. And you can scarcely see your hand before your face. I'm not letting my father come. I just about had to tie him up, but he's not fit for it. I hope yours has more sense. It's not a day for man or beast to be out, unless he's young. I don't know when I'll get to speak to your father—if this keeps on, not for days. I'll try to come down to-night, if we're home in time, just for a moment to make sure the wind hasn't blown you clean away. Usual time, usual place; if it's very rough don't come out, just think of me and I'll think of you—oh well, I'm always and forever doing that, so promising it isn't any great catch.

ARCHIE.

6

The Same to the Same

Dear, dear Rose, can you come up at once?
Your father is here, safe and sound—sound
asleep, I think. We're sending George down
with this letter. Would you believe it, Dad
himself wanted to go, because you'd be worrying. George is taking two horses and will bring
you up, at the gallop, he promises me. Honey,
if you came on the wings of the wind it wouldn't
be fast enough. Your father is safe and sound
but very tired. He had a terrible day. I found
him in the Gar corrie, completely dead-beat and
lost. I'm keeping George waiting and that
means you're waiting and worrying, but I've
got to waste time, I can't keep it to myself any
longer. When I found your father in the Gar
corrie he agreed to our marrying. MARRYING.
You and me! You see, I managed to ask him
to-day after all. When you come up, and see
your father, and speak to him, he'll tell you,
and then I'll ask you 'Rose, beloved, when'—
stroke out ~~when~~, like that, and put in 'how
soon'—'how soon will we get married? We've

our fathers' blessings.' The two of them spent half an hour telling each other how wrong it would be to stand in the young people's way! God bless all storms, blizzards, and rough corries. I'm so excited and happy I don't know whether to cry or sing or go running in circles in the snowdrift. Hurry, hurry, Rose.

ARCHIE.

7

Mrs Lockhart, the Manse, to Mrs Maisie Dalgarno, Edinburgh

MY DEAR MAISIE,

We have just come in from our afternoon walk, where we met young Archie Cameron and heard the nicest bit of news we've heard since we came here. You remember my telling you of the ancient feud between Archie's father and Robert Sinclair? At Christmas-time it blazed out with fresh fury over some wretched sheep that had strayed from Cameron's place on to Sinclair's ground. Nothing would suit our stiff-necked elders but that they would go to law over it. What made them more furious with each other was that their children were in love with each other and were in the habit of using the manse glebe as a trysting place, and of course this couldn't go on indefinitely without some busybody telling their parents about it. George was nearly distracted with worry over it all, but neither of the men would relent, and really at the beginning of this month things looked set for not one but *two* desperate lawsuits. Now, thank goodness, it's all right, and there's to be no litigation but a grand wedding instead.

Young Archie is quite off his head with excitement and joy, and he told us the whole story when we met him this afternoon. It seems he had matters out with his father about his marrying Rose Sinclair. Old Cameron went so far as to say that if Robert Sinclair agreed to the match he would not withhold his consent. With this very grudging blessing (for, of course, the noble King Cameron was quite sure Sinclair would refuse), Archie wrote Sinclair a note proposing to call on him on such and such a day. For a wonder, Sinclair agreed to this, but before Archie could get down, there came the first real storm of the winter. You'll have seen about it in the papers, I'm sure. It was very wild; I never heard such wind, or saw such drifts of snow. Archie could not think of going to Shirramore, because he had to go out and rescue his poor dumb wandered sheep instead. It so happened that Robert Sinclair went out that day also to care for his own beasts, and he got lost and dead-beat, for he's not so young as he once was—a thing he, like all men, refuses to realise. (Archie said he had practically to tie his own father down to keep him from coming to the hill too.) Well, when poor Rose saw no sign of her father coming home she sent word down the glen, and a search-party was arranged by our new Aberdonian neighbour, Watt, who, whatever folk may say about him being hard, has certainly got organising ability. It was rather sad to see the way his crofter neighbours followed his direction in the emergency, so Janet says, anyway. While all this was going on, Archie had already stumbled across Sinclair by the sheerest and, of course, happiest accident. The old man was lying almost exhausted behind a rock, and, storm or not, Archie, the young rascal, saw at once he had a Heaven-sent opportunity, and forthwith he demanded Sinclair's consent to his own and

Rose's marriage. That's a very ruthless young man, Maisie, and I think Rose will not suffer from boredom in days to come. 'I just told him that I was going to rescue him whether or not,' said the bold Archie. 'I said I could and would rescue him, dead or alive. If I brought him home alive it would be very difficult for him to refuse to let me have Rose, for very shame's sake, because he'd owe me his life, and if he kept up his feud against me after that he'd be namely through the whole land, and I'd help to make him so. On the other hand, if I rescued him dead it would be still more difficult for him to refuse.' My dear, I was delighted to hear Archie's news, but, do you know, I was a little bit appalled too, and sorry for Sinclair. How brutal the young are, especially the *Cameron* young. When Archie told us his story he stuck out his jaw just like his father, and I could imagine him looking perfectly terrifying to that poor Sinclair lying exhausted in the snow.

Well, Archie told Sinclair that he had his father's consent and then the hero insinuated that since old Cameron gave his consent simply to embarrass Sinclair, whom he did not expect ever to agree, the best way of spiting our King was to consent and catch him fairly in his own little trap. At that Sinclair actually laughed, the first time he's laughed or even smiled in a Cameron's presence for years, and then he caved in completely, whereupon Archie got him upon his shoulders and carried him to his own home at Kerrow. Archie himself makes light of his task, but I can't think how he managed to carry Sinclair over such treacherous ground in such awful weather. However, he did, sometimes carrying him, sometimes dragging him—or so Archie said—and at last he electrified them all at Kerrow by staggering in with his father's prize enemy in his arms. Before old Alexander could utter a word Archie informed him over the semi-conscious Sinclair that he'd got his consent to his marrying Rose and they might all as well shake hands and be friends because, of course, there could be no question now of lawsuits or keeping up the feud either. Well, they did shake hands, actually in a friendly way, though with rather wry looks at their taskmaster Archie, and after that word was sent to Rose, while Sinclair himself was put to bed. He stayed awake just long enough to tell noble Alexander very firmly that they must not stand between their young people and happiness. And now Sinclair is well enough to be home again at Shirramore, while the whole place is ringing with the joyful news that the old wretched spiteful affair is over and instead of lawsuits there'll be this famous wedding. It's to be some time in April, Archie says, and as far as I can gather the entire glen is to be invited. I can tell you there never was a more blessed storm. We ourselves are happy for the young people's sake, and also for our own sakes, because a bitter quarrel between George's leading elders was a constant worry and grief. But it will really make a great difference for the whole glen. People used to take sides, and little quarrels flourished in the shadow of the big one. More than once, I'm told, the shepherds of the rival farmers came to blows out of a mistaken feeling of fidelity to their masters.

This news has really eclipsed all other doings here, but I mustn't forget to say that returning spring is inspiring other folk than the Camerons and Sinclairs. My dear Shamus Munro, after pestering everybody, and Janet in especial, to

give him old aluminium hot-water bottles and
kettles, which he was collecting, for the government, as he declared, in his new rôle of scrap-
merchant, suddenly blossomed out with an old
car. Everybody wondered very much where
he got the money to buy and license and insure
it, and it's been going round that Mrs Macaskill
the Shop lent him cash. In any case, she's been
very smug and cryptic whenever people spoke
about Shamus. Well, the next thing was that
Shamus built a trailer for his car. Such a con-
traption it was! And such hammering he had
when he was making it, you could hear the din
above the howling of the loudest storms, but
for all the hammering it seemed to me to be
held together mainly with wires and bits of
rope. Then Shamus came out of his retire-
ment and spent a few days making his rounds
in pursuit of scrap, though, as Watt, the Aberdonian, very cruelly said, he didn't get much
because, firstly, the people here are keeping their
old junk, since they think they can make their
own fortunes out of it, and secondly, all the old
bed-ends are needed for gates. So Shamus
didn't get a great deal, and what he did get
he paid far too much for from a fat and most

mysterious roll of the things our Highland neighbours gravely call 'paper pound-notes.' And
then he vanished into the blue, and no one
knew where, except possibly Nell Macaskill,
who became more mysterious and complacent
than ever about his doings. I asked her if she
had heard from Shamus, and all she deigned
to reply was: 'Mrs Lockhart, there is more in
Shamus than some folks think. One of these
days he will be surprising us all.' But oh, dear,
nothing Shamus could do would surprise me,
unless he turned sensible and started to work for
his living. Poor foolish pet!

George is so uplifted at the solution of the
Cameron-Sinclair imbroglio that he is more
set than ever on that pet scheme of his for building the new hall by voluntary labour. Well,
I'm not too happy about that, especially since
my experience in organising that compara-
tively minor affair the concert we held before
Christmas. We are going to hold a grand sale
of work in aid of the hall funds some time this
autumn. It is to be held in Inverartney, because
we've no place here at all suitable and the people
say one must have it when the 'toffs' are here,
and the weather's too unchancy then for an out-

of-doors affair. It'll be a business transporting everything down to Inverartney, though we can't do anything else, and Inverartney has very kindly offered us the loan of its hall for the event. I'm to do the cake and candy along with Mrs Macaskill. I hope she'll keep Shamus away until it's over, otherwise he'll be running us in for quite impossible plans. Now no more. Much love from your affectionate friend

ALICE.

P.S.—I suppose you've no really good notions for the work stall? They're all set on embroidering tea-cloths and so on here, and you never get your own out of these interminable embroideries.

A. L.

MARCH

1

DEAR SHAMUS,

I am sending by this post the iron lists you wrote for, hoping you will get same all right Post Restante Inverartney. I will send any more c/o P.O. Auchmore like you said. I hope you are getting on all right collecting plenty iron for the Govt. There's been a great speak in the Strath here about your business but I never let on, for it's not good for them just to know everything. There's many a one has come in for a stamp that never writes a letter from one year's end to another, but I'm fit for them, Shamus, I can tell you. Even the minister's wife was hinting about your business. She has a great notion of your cleverness —not like some I could mention but won't.

You heard the news about the Sinclairs and the Camerons being friends. Isn't it nice Archie

176

and Rose getting married? There is nothing new here at all, but I'm hearing that Robert Sinclair is giving Rose a lot of money for her tocher. Thousands is what they are saying, but likely it will not be as much. There's no more lawyers' letters going whatever, which is a blessing. Young Archie Cameron was in bye with a letter to big jewellers in London. Likely he will be getting the ring from the south though there's nothing registered come yet. He was asking would you and me be coming to his marriage, Shamus. He is not proud like his father. I will be expecting a letter from you by return, Shamus, saying about the iron. See you and take care of yourself now when you are away and be getting good lodgings for a lot is depending on you. By the papers I see the world is in an awful state, that's foreigners for you, but you will know yourself about them, having seen them in their native quarters. I am missing you coming in for a crack, especially as the P.O. is very dull the now, the football coupons being near stopped. Hoping you are in the pink, with kind regards,

yours truly,

NELL.

P.S.—I cannot work the wringer yet, but hope you will explain it when you get back. The mangle is a great miss but once the govt. work is over you will maybe take a right look at it.

2

The Same to the Same

DEAR SHAMUS,

Am surprised no letter. Did I not told you to write by return? It is not right of you, Shamus. I hope you got my letter all right. I sent it where you told me. I am saying to myself, Nell, it is not right of you worrying Shamus when he is on govt. work, but I would like a letter saying All is going Good. I went to see Alistair Og to ask had he word from you, but No! Here is more prices from iron dealers. I see they are offering high prices so am hoping you will deal with them. Hoping you are keeping fine yourself and getting a lot of iron,

your old friend,

NELL.

3

The Same to the Same

Shamus, are you dead ? Where are you ? No letters from you and you away ten days. Maybe your car is over a precipice and you lying dead in it. Please write and say. If you don't I will need to go to the minister and ask him for to advise me about burying you which will be difficult owing to you having all my money but I wouldn't have it said that Shamus Munro was buried on the parish. Write at once.

NELL.

4

March 16

Rev. George Lockhart to The Postmaster, Auchmore

DEAR SIR,

I am writing on behalf of the friends in this glen of a James (or Shamus) Munro, who left here some little time ago and gave instructions that letters to him should be addressed, or readdressed,

c/o the Post-Office,

Auchmore.

These instructions were followed, and several important letters demanding an answer were sent c/o your office to Munro, but all have so far elicited no reply. His friends are naturally anxious and distressed with the fear that some accident has befallen him. He is no longer a young man, and they are afraid he may be unable to collect letters at your Post-Office, or to reply. I should be most obliged if you found it possible, and consistent with your regulations, to let me know whether the letters addressed to Munro have been called for by a man answering to this description :

James or Shamus Munro; aged about 50; short, slightly built; bald; fresh complexion; very large aquiline nose, large blue eyes. Dressed probably in hoddengray knickerbocker suit and deer-stalker hat.

If you are able to give me the information I desire it will relieve Munro's friends' minds and save them from applying to the police for help, which you will understand is the last thing they would wish to do, since Munro may be well and safe.

I am,

Yours faithfully,

GEORGE LOCKHART,

Parish Minister.

5

March 18

The Same to the Same

DEAR MR ROBERTSON,

Many thanks for your kind and courteous reply. I am deeply relieved to learn that Munro is safe and sound. Yes, the man you describe is him exactly. He is very fond of discussing his business abroad in various parts of the world when he was younger. Your saying that he offered to buy the Post-Office's used copper telegraph wiring clinches the question. Again many thanks.

Yours sincerely,

GEORGE LOCKHART.

6

March 18

The Same to Shamus Munro, c/o Post-Office, Auchmore

MY DEAR SHAMUS,

Mrs Macaskill called upon me in very deep distress to tell me about your absence and your failure to answer her letters. She was so distressed, indeed, and afraid you had met with an accident, that I took the liberty of writing to the postmaster at Auchmore to discover whether you had collected your letters. I was informed that you had, and therefore I write to you in the confidence that this note will reach you, and be read and, I sincerely hope, attended to, and thus we may escape the disagreeable necessity of putting out an official S O S and of asking the police to help us find you, with all the difficulties and unpleasantness such a course would entail.

Mrs Macaskill explained the whole situation to me, and though I think it was foolish of her to entrust her entire life's savings to you to venture upon such a speculative and, indeed, hare-brained project as this scrap-collecting scheme of yours, yet I am sure that your failure to answer her letters has been due to misfortune or trickery overtaking you and depriving you of the money, rather than to any intention to defraud.

Nevertheless, Shamus, cowardice, moral cowardice, and unwillingness to face up to the consequences of one's follies do, if carried far enough, assume the aspect of dishonourable conduct. If you have lost, or been robbed or cheated of, Mrs Macaskill's money, as I half fear, half hope, it will not be easy for you to take the straight and honourable course of returning to Strathmazeran to own up to your defeat. But, and I say this with the fullest force I can use, you must do so, and at once, both for her sake and your own, and to avoid the scandal that will certainly follow if you fail to return. If you fail to return—there will certainly be trouble, I promise that. But at the moment we need not discuss a situation which I pray will not arise. Only, remember that the possibility of an exceedingly difficult problem arising for you is there.

Now, Mrs Macaskill is very, very fond of you. She came to me because she was grieved with fear you had been hurt or killed in some accident. And I think it sufficiently indicates her magnanimity and her liking for you when I say that the chief cause of her fearing and regretting the loss of all her hard-earned money which she entrusted to you was that if you were hurt she had nothing left to spend on your care; if you were dead, she had nothing wherewith to bury you decently. Mrs Macaskill is a woman in ten thousand, and you are very, very fortunate to have her friendship, which I trust you will never again abuse.

I pooh-poohed her fears, being convinced in my own mind that matters were otherwise than she imagined; I believe that pride, not death or injury, keeps you from coming home to confess that you have not succeeded in your scrap-iron venture. I take this opportunity to warn you—and I hope I need never do it again —against the blind and besetting sin of pride. In any case, no matter what has happened, Mrs Macaskill will be too happy to see you again to blame you, which it is not in her nature to do. You are already forgiven, if ever you were really blamed. Will you therefore write at once to Mrs Macaskill, telling her what has happened, and asking her forgiveness. And advise me immediately you have written her.

Nothing that has happened need be made known in the glen, if we keep our own counsel, which I shall do, and Mrs Macaskill certainly will always do. The whole story can remain a closed book to all except us three. As I said, Mrs Macaskill is very fond of you. The only thing she holds against you is the deprivation of her mangle. For the rest, she will welcome you dearly. But when you come home you must for your own sake mend that mangle! Women never forget trifling things; it is the larger sins and follies they so generously wipe from their minds. Now I have written at length. I want to make it clear that you are not returning to a glen full of malicious gossip. And also to make it clear that you must return. As your pastor, I should in justice adopt a more severe tone than I have. But I think, and pray, that you have learned a lasting lesson.

I am, Shamus,

your pastor,

GEORGE LOCKHART.

7

March 21

Mrs Nell Macaskill to Shamus Munro,
Poste Restante, Auchmore

DEAR SHAMUS,

Got your letter. It's a God's blessing you are not dead and I am very thankful. Don't you be worrying over that dirty trash Tod MacAfee the hawker that cheated you. What a thing to do! To sell you a great bing of iron that didn't belong to him at all, at all, and then to leave you alone to buy it all over again from him that really owned it. It was bad of him Shamus, but what can you expect from a tinker that's father was a tinker and tinker again to the third and fourth generation. If I had him I would give him *thon*, so I would. The Rev. Lockhart says that them that's honest don't know the cheatery tricks of the dishonest, and it's just because you're an honest man without guile, as the Good Book says, that Tod MacAfee deceived and cheated you. The next time he comes round seeking rabbit-skins is it skins I will give him? No, but such a skelp, and that'll sort him, so it will.

No, Shamus, I do not think you and me should go to New Zealand like you say just because folk will talk. If you ask me they will talk in New Zealand just the same as in Strathmazeran. Anyway, nobody will say anything about you and the way MacAfee cheated you, the low, lying puppy that he is, because not a soul here but me and the minister and his wife knows anything about it, and none of us will say a word.

Shamus, was you thinking when you said I should come with you to New Zealand that we should mebbe perhaps be going as man and wife? Though I don't think we should go to foreign parts I wouldn't mind mebbe being Mrs Munro. It would be a change for me, and then you would mend my mangle, it being in a manner of speaking your mangle as well.

Now, never mind about the money. We will make any's the amount when you come back. They are fair stuck about the Hall till you come home for to advise them so you better come quick. I am enclosing P.O. for 12/6 for your fare home. You can tell them that asks that you sold car and trailer to the govt. for bombs. It is a good thing there are men like you in this country. If they was all Tod MacAfees we would be away with it inside of a week. I will expect you to your tea the day you come back.

Your old friend,

NELL.

8

March 26

Miss Janet Colthart to Mrs Katherine Hamilton, Peebles

MY DEAR SISTER,

I am fair relieved to hear that your flu is over and the weans are better too. We have managed

187

through the winter fine ourselves, though the minister had a bad cold in November. This place agrees with us all grand, though quite a few of the natives have been down with various ills of one sort or another. What can you expect? They have no stamina, owing to them drinking tea even on and not having decent solid meals at regular hours. Slipshod, that's what they are.

Well, we've been having quite a steery time one way or another. I told you, if I remember right, about the Camerons and the Sinclairs being friends and the great marriage that's coming off. I am real pleased and said so to Miss Sinclair when I met her down the village the other day. She is a bonny lass, and a real lady to speak to. She was telling me her granny came from the Borders. I thought she wasn't all Highland. She told me, too, that she was hoping I would be at her wedding. I said of course I would be in the church that day, but it seems she wanted me to come on to the reception as well. She said she would see I got my invitation with all particulars on it. The reception is to be at her father's home. I don't know when I took such a notion to a Highland person, though of course her granny being from the Borders makes a difference.

Then there's very nice sensible folk come from Aberdeenshire to a place called Croft Roy. Watt is their name, and Mrs Watt asked me up to my tea my last day off. They have four nice bairns, too, and everything was spotless. She is near as good a hand at the girdle scones as you are yourself, Katie, and that's saying something. Her man is a great worker and has the place looking as neat outside as she has it inside. I didn't see very much of him, as he was at his work till six o'clock. So different to the men here, who are just sitting about their wives' kitchens drinking tea from dawn till dark. Mrs Watt and me had a right good talk, and I told her a few things about the place here. I also told her that the mistress would take her eggs, milk, butter, and cream from her. Just now we're getting them from the Maclagans, and it's most unsatisfactory. For one thing their hens have just begun to lay, and they don't seem able to work their cows right for we are only getting a dribble of milk, and not very clean at that. In fact, during the winter months we were actually using tinned milk. That ever I should see the day! Mind you, there's this about the tin, it's *clean*. The Watts will also supply vegetables. The minister was saying that he would delve the garden and grow everything we needed. Of course that's just all nonsense, because I don't believe he knows the difference between a graip and a hoe. He thought of getting Willie Mitchell to help him, but I doubt if Mitchell can keep off the drink long enough.

I didn't tell you in my last, did I, about the wee concert Watt and Mackie ran for the Hall they're to build here. A very different affair from the one at Christmas where there was no organisation at all. Mackie is the schoolmaster and comes from the same place as Watt. Everything ran to time-table I can assure you. There were footlights and a stage which Mackie fixed up. He even had a man sitting under the petrol lamp. Before the affair started at a given word this man had to lower the lamp and put it out. Just at that very moment the footlights went on. Then at the end there was another cue and he had to light the lamp. Clockwork wasn't in it.

There's one thing nobody can say about the folk here and that is that they're mean. They have collected quite a lot of money amongst them, and next month the work on the hall is to start. I am told that the architect, a Mr Thompson from Aberdeen, is to be there. He's gey fond of coming here with no excuse at all, so I expect he'll be fair delighted to come for such a reason. Miss Davidson at Cairnbeg, where he stays when he comes, and himself are real thick. She's a quiet wee thing, but *still waters*, you know, Katie.

There's been a lot of mysterious goings-on at the P.O. with Mrs Macaskill and that pet of hers Shamus Munro who stole a tea-pot from my kitchen. He disappeared for several weeks and now that he is home nobody knows right what happened him. He went away with a car and trailer to collect scrap-iron by his way of it. Now he's home without car or trailer and it's put out that he's had an accident. That's as may be. Willie Mitchell said that he'd been and embezzled money from the P.O. and was now in hiding from the law and *that* was his accident. Mitchell said as much to Alick Maclagan, who got up in an awful rage and was for thrashing Mitchell. It's been a great speak here, and though Willie Mitchell isn't as truthful as many a one, there's aye some water where the stirkie droons, as the old saying is. But the reason I'm not on for believing Mitchell is that the minister was very angry when he heard the rumours Mitchell was putting out and spoke very severely to him about it. I'm hearing too that Shamus and Mrs Macaskill are to make a match of it. If so she must be mad for a man. At her age, it's scandalous. There may be nothing in it, of course, but you never know.

I don't think I've any more news except that I'm on the committee for giving teas to the men who are to put up the hall. It's the locals that are to do it, by the minister's wish. It's an awful nuisance when saints, and the master is a saint, gets a bee in their bonnet. Well, I suppose we'll just have to thole it, but I'll see they work for their tea. It's either talk or tea, but there's not to be both.

Do you think I should get a new hat for the Sinclair wedding? The hats just now are that queer it's a thought to buy one. Not but what I like to be as smart as the next, but this *chic* the papers are all going on about is just French for indecent. Let me know what you think.

Ever your affectionate sister,

JANET.

9

March 30
Alistair Og Maclagan to Shamus Munro

Shamus, my old friend! what has come over
you, where are you hiding? How can Hall go
on and Shamus not there? Man, you should
not let the glen down. I was sorry you hurt
your leg in that bad smash when the car ran
off down a cliff and you caught hold on a tree.
Ach, well, it is a mercy you were spared, for
many a one would not have come out of it in
one bit. I got a sight of you through the glass.
You are very cripple, man; likely it will follow
you all the days of your life. When a man is
not so young it is worse on him. My own
father was like that till the day he died. All the
same you can walk and every man that can walk
should be on his feet now, especially you, Shamus,
to get on with Hall. So now come up here
quick. I am telling you straight, come up here
quick or I will be angry, you know me, I do
not make two faces but it's straight out every
time. We are depending on you. That Watt
ran a concert by his way of it—ach, Mackie did

it all but he never let on, him coming from the same place. Some folk have a bold face on them, come in here a week or two and then—never heed, you will be at the head of things as of old. Were they telling you I had words with that weed Willie Mitchell? Another Aberdonian, the place is stinking with them. I gave him a bit of my mind. No man will say wrong of Shamus Munro in front of my face. But it is not easy Shamus if you hide yourself out of sight. Now, look here, you would not like the Hall to be made wrong? I have the plans you drawed, but what good is that when you're not there. I have not the gift. Is it true you and Nell Macaskill are getting married to each other? I will be looking for a invite and a good howpie of the Hard for to drink your health. Ach well, she is not that old when you come to think of it. My own mother was near ninety when she died. Mebbe Shamus it is love that is wrong with you, making you hide, shy, mebbe you are writing love poetry like the verses you showed me, Bonny Strathmazeran. Many is the one I told them to since thon day you first spoke them. You didn't ought to be keeping it from your old friend Alistair if that is what. I will

look forward to hearing them. Nell will be
knowing them, I must make on I have a letter
going. Och, I'm just teasing you. Shamus,
love is awful, but do not let it spoil our Hall on
us. You can do both, I know it. That is what
I always say, Shamus can do anything. So come
up quick.

ALISTAIR.

10

March 31
Charles Watt, Croft Roy, to Roderick Maclean,
Craggan

DEAR MR MACLEAN,

Many thanks for the kind invite and we will
come up at the time you say. It will be a great
bother to you owing to there being so many of
us and it is very good of you to ask us all. The
bairns are looking forward to it a fair treat I can
tell you. Mrs Watt is looking forward to meeting Mrs Maclean also. There is this W.R.I.
which is to be started. She is keen on that and
is hoping Mrs Maclean is keen. I think there
will be a great claiking when the two women
get their heads thegither.

I was just passing the remark to Mrs Watt,

195

and I would say it though I was back in my own parts again, folk with us in Aberdeenshire do not make in-comers welcome the way you do here. I am feeling I would like to help in the glen if I could, just as a sort of paying off for the kindness we got since Mrs Watt came. That is the way I am, Mr Maclean, independent by nature; I do not like to be under an obligation without paying it back, which is the best way for folk in my thinking. Help them that helps you.

Now, re co-operative, I'm sair feared it's not practicable to have a real affair. A secretary would need £50 a year anyway, and it cannot be done. Now, I have gone over it in my mind what we can do and I have taken the chance to approach one man and another, and to cut a long tale short, if one man, or two men here, say you and me atween us, got orders for manures and seeds and feeding-stuffs from all the folk that wanted to buy keen, we could send them off under our own name to the North-Eastern Co-operative in Aberdeen, which is a very good firm and I am a member. I would say they would maybe quote a price two-thirds what it is locally. Now that would be a big saving for the folk round about. You will be saying to yourself, Aye, but what am I getting out of it but the bother and the risk? There'll be that anyway, as you know fine, and we'll just have to settle atween us Is it worth it? If so, then you and me would have the bonus. Last year it was 2s. 8d. in the pound on manures and seeds, 1s. 8d. on the pound feeding-stuff. You get it in cash or goods.

Mind you, Mr Maclean, we will better keep this wee matter under our thumb as you might say, for if the folk that was buying heard, you know what folk are, they'd grudge it and go elsewhere and pay more rather than see us make a penny out of them, even though we was taking the risk of them not being good for their money. But we will see we do not take foolish risks. It is a bad thing to encourage bad payers. Make them pay cash is my motto, it is for their own good. I am sure Rev. Lockhart would say ditto. But we will keep this about bonus to our nain selves. I've seen it afore, men will pay dear and give the dealer 6/8 in the pound sooner than see a neighbour earn a maik out of them. Mind you, the bonus is not much. If we were dealing right we'd be taking 25% or even $33\frac{1}{3}\%$.

We will also speak about one more thing. When the news gets round we are dealing with Co-op. all the dealers will be bizzing like red-hipped bees. They will cut their prices, do you see. Will the folk stand by us then, do you think? That is the question.

I have prices. It might be a good thing to call a wee meeting. If we got Rev. Lockhart in the chair that would take a trick. Folk like it when the man at the head has not got anything to gain out of them. I will tackle him if you think it would be worth it. I know fine he is interested. He was asking me about this very thing last time I met him.

A place like this should have a branch of the Bee-keepers' Association. I am wondering you here never started that. Mind me to tell you the name of the firm that is looking for women to knit stockings. That'll keep them at home on the winter nights instead of running out for a gossip!

We will put these things through hand when I come up. I will say right out I am fair stounded at the prices you are all paying. You are working three hours a day to gie the dealers and merchants yon bonny red faces they have. Take

coal, now—but I will say the price I think right
when I come up.

Yours truly,

CHARLES WATT.

Glad you liked concert.

11

March 31

*Margaret Davidson, Cairnbeg, to
John Thompson, Aberdeen*

DEAR MR THOMPSON,

You've no idea how thrice-welcome your
great hamper of flowers was. A flower means
such a lot to us here, where spring comes reluct-
antly and with so many false starts that occasion-
ally we feel like giving up hope. Now with
the house full of your mimosa and violets we
can forget the dull landscape outside. Not that
we are without any sign of spring, tho'. The
peesies are back and are making a fearful fuss
beyond the steading, and the curlews are crying
above the moor. To Morrison the gamekeeper's
fury the sea-gulls are up too, and are getting
ready to nest in the wee loch. Morrison is chew-

ing his moustache and vowing vengeance on their eggs. He says that the gulls eat his precious grouse eggs and he'll show them what's what, even if they *are* protected. To-morrow he's arranged a fox-hunt, and every male in the glen seems to be taking part in it. He issued written instructions to all the shepherds in the place as to where they were to go, where to shout and where to be quiet. The keepers will be armed with rifles and are to beat the wood at the west end of the wee loch. I don't expect they'll get anything there, because they never do—but they never stop trying. It's a tradition. Isn't it funny; if this were England we'd have huntsmen and red coats and hounds and all sorts of picturesqueness, but here the master of the hounds is your old friend Alistair Og, who assuredly won't wear a red coat, but will be attired in a Balaclava helmet and rubber boots and his old patchedest jacket, waistcoat, and plus-fours, all of different suits, naturally. And there won't be any horses, and the hounds will be mongrel terriers and the shepherds' collies. As for huntsmen's horns, the voices of the Cairnbeg shepherds will supply that, not Yoicks or Tally-ho, but a sort of yipping, like this—Hey-yip! Yo ho hey yip! Hey-yea-yea-yip! Hoy! We've got three shepherds from the West just now with the loudest voices I ever heard. Father says they can work their dogs three miles away without getting up from their beds! They seem to take a deep breath in the morning and bawl continuously all day till night, when they draw their next breath.

I suppose you'll have got the official particulars about the hall from Mr Lockhart or Mr Mackie. Watt, the new crofter in Croft Roy, who comes from the same district as Mackie, went down to the schoolhouse the other week, and he and Mackie drew up time-tables for the voluntary workers who are going to build the hall, leaving blank spaces for names. Then they stuck one time-table up on the church door and sent two to the post-office, and gave out that any one who liked could fill in his name, but he'd be expected to hold to the hours he promised. Watt put his own name down for so many hours with a horse and cart that everybody else in jealousy put their names down too with hours to eclipse his, and then Watt and Mackie made the women responsible for giving tea to so many workers, a gang, as it were.

Mackie worked on the women's pride by getting as many of her own relatives as possible into each gangeress's band, and by telling them he would depend on them to see that there were no malingerers. It was all done very cleverly and cunningly indeed, and I think we'll be hearing more of our Mr Watt.

Shamus Munro enrolled himself promptly for three nights a week 'in advisory capacity.' I'm wondering what Alistair Og will do? Poor Ali, won't he be torn between his own laziness and his desire to make a big one of himself! Dad is sending a man with a horse and cart several hours a week, and so are Cameron and Sinclair. The Cameron-Sinclair wedding is, of course, the speak in the glen just now. The invitations aren't out yet, but I expect the entire countryside will be invited.

A lesser entertainment, but one fairly *bristling* with mystery, is the Affair of Shamus Munro the Scrap Merchant and Mrs Macaskill the Post-Office. I told you of him going off complete with car and trailer to make his fortune in the great wide world. Well, he's home again, sans car, sans trailer, and sans fortune. It's reported that he had an accident with his car and just saved himself from death either by clinging to a handy tree which grew on the lip of a precipice or by swimming a mile in a stormy sea. Take your choice; both stories are said to have come from Shamus himself, and he should know. His car, of course, either hurled itself over the abyss or preferably into the depths of the sea, where it would vanish and leave no unwelcome questions regarding its whereabouts. It is also reported that he lured Mrs Macaskill into giving him post-office money to finance his venture and now he's concealing himself from the law. And still another tale is that he was cheated out of everything by hawkers called MacAfee. No one has seen more than glimpses of him since his return, tho' Alistair Og put the telescope on him and reports that he was limping badly. Willie Mitchell the beadle very nastily said that Shamus wasn't limping when he came home— in fact, he didn't start limping until he'd thought up the accident story; at which Alistair threatened to thrash Wullock. Anyway, Shamus can't be very ill because he'd got his name down at the post-office, as I told you.

We'll be expecting you on April 13th, then. Mr Mackie will be sending you the date of the celebration—I think it's the 20th. It's true, isn't it, that you're to be invited to lay the foundation-stone—or is it plant the first railway sleeper? Whatever it is, you know how we'll be looking forward to seeing you. The fishing will be on by that time.

With best thanks and kindest wishes from us all,

Yours sincerely,
MARGARET DAVIDSON.

Dad has just come in from being at the post-office. You'll be pleased to learn that the work Alistair is going to do in building the hall is 'Put myself at Mr Thompson's personal disposal for fishing or other, 4 nights per week, yours truly, A. MACLAGAN.' Isn't he cute?

M.

APRIL

I

April 2

Adam Mackie, the Schoolhouse, to
John Thompson, Aberdeen

DEAR MR THOMPSON,

It is excellent news that you are coming to help us start work on the hall when we make our official beginning on the 20th of this month. We are all delighted, and very much indebted to you for coming so far to give us the benefit of your skilled advice. We are arranging a little ceremony in which I think you will be asked to dig the first sod or something of that nature. I hope this is agreeable to you. Have you made arrangements where you will stay? If not, my wife hopes you will put up with us. I have been told you are going to Cairnbeg, but in any case there must be no question of your lodging at the Hotel.

Alistair Maclagan, your old ghillie, has declared that his work for the hall will be helping you to catch fish! I am sure we all hope you succeed in getting some sport, both with Alistair and with the trout.

Yours sincerely,

ADAM MACKIE.

2

April 4

Adam Mackie to The Glen

A NOTICE

The foundations of the new hall will be laid out on April 20th at 2.30 p.m. Mr Thompson, architect for the hall, has kindly agreed to perform the ceremony of marking out the site, and it is hoped that as many people as possible will attend to welcome him and indicate our gratitude for his very generous aid.

ADAM MACKIE,
Secretary,
General Committee for
Strathmazeran Public Hall.

April 4

Shamus Munro to Rev. George Lockhart

DEAR MR LOCKHART DEAR SIR,

I am writing to thank you for all you did for me showing me what was right. Dear Mr Lockhart I will never do the like again, it was a lesson. I am settling down the way you said, it is not right always to be roving. I would come up but I do not like. There is a matter of a tea-pot I think I must have taken by mistake out of your kitchen, that's what she says that you have in it. I tried the metal-merchants. I said 'Send me back tea-pot quick.' No answer. It is not right of them. But I will replace it without fail or make up the price, work for it, I can beat carpets beautiful, also tease mattrass. I hope you are getting on with hall. It is a godsend there is men like you building halls and keeping folk right in this bad world all full of nasty cheats. I am sorry I was a bother but will not be again. I will devote myself to my own jobs which is engineering eckceckera. A man that is honest has no chance with rascals. Oh, that Tod Mac-

Afee! Lucky was I he left the clothes on me.
I will mind him all the days of my life. Nell
and me—ach, excuse me, what am I saying, Mrs
Macaskill I should be saying—we are thinking of
getting married if you have no objection. She
told me Ask him will he do it, marry us. She
is a good woman. I will be happy working for
her. Will you put out banns ect. at your best
convenience. Tell Janet I will get a better tea-
pot, bigger, thon one was too small. Or I will
tease mattrass. We were thinking April 29 would
be nice for getting married. Very quiet affair.
Thanking you very much,

yours obediently,
SHAMUS MUNRO.

4

April 10

Robert Sinclair to Everybody

Robert Sinclair, Shirramore, invites the pleasure of your company at the marriage of his
daughter Rose to Archibald, son of Alexander
Cameron, Kerrow, at Strathmazeran parish

church at 2.30 p.m. April 24th, and afterwards at Shirramore.

R.S.V.P.

5

April 12

Alexander Cameron, Kerrow, to
Robert Sinclair, Shirramore

MY DEAR SINCLAIR,

Can I take you down to Inverartney on Monday? I am sending a fat beast to the sale and would like to see it sold. In any case, I'll call past and drop Archie at Shirramore, where he seems anxious to call!

This weather should bring on the grass nicely. Did the storm do much damage with you? My own ewes have picked up wonderfully.

Yours sincerely,

ALEXANDER CAMERON.

I think we ought to discuss together, and with Davidson Cairnbeg, how we can assist Lockhart to build his hall.

I believe the invitations have just gone out. I begin to feel very old and lonely!

April 14

*John Thompson, at Cairnbeg, to his
Housekeeper in Aberdeen*

DEAR MRS BENZIE,

I find that I have to stay on here longer than I expected, and shan't be back until next week. I'll advise you when to expect me. I wonder if you'd be so good as to send me some clean clothes; you know what I'll need for a week's stay. Will you also send *at once* my dinner-jacket suit with all the appurtenances. I hope you are enjoying the same lovely spring weather as we have here.

Yours sincerely,

JOHN THOMPSON.

7

April 14

Archie Cameron to Rose Sinclair

DEAREST ROSE,

Isn't it awful, I've got so into the way of writing you from the days when we couldn't meet openly that now I can't stop. I feel there's something wrong because I amn't sending you surreptitious letters, and getting letters back from you by the secretive—and open—hand of James the Post. In fact, it's all I can do to keep myself from sneaking out and waylaying Jimmy with this note itself. And he, poor pet, is quite at a loss—in more senses than one, the drunken darling. He looks at me with such reproach in his eyes when I've nothing for you—or for him, by the same token. Ah, what a thing is love! It helped to paint Jimmy's nose ruby, and now the paint-pot's drying up. Can you wonder he looks sad? Och, it's a shame to make fun of poor Jimmy; what would we have done without him in the sad harried wild blissful days gone past, when every moment we had together was stolen from parents, duty, and—I must really stop letter-writing sometime. It's not done in the best married circles. My goodness, you couldn't have man and wife writing each other billets-doux, could you? Or getting James the Post to sneak them from one room to another!

Darling, the days go creeping past, and in how many, is it ten, we'll be MR and MRS ARCHIBALD CAMERON. Oh, no, indeed, I will not have them calling you 'Mrs Archibald.' Rose—Rose Cameron—Rose anything if it's you. Any name's bonny that's yours. Did I say I was madly and wildly infatuated with you? Think of that, and him confessing it too, boasting about it, and him not needing to do it any more seeing he's getting married to the woman. Darling, if ever sheep were herded with wild and joyful excitement, Kerrow sheep are at this blessed moment undergoing that strange experience. Every time I see them wandering on to Shirramore ground I say to myself 'Damn it, Archie, who are you to blame them for that?' Oh, they should go on their bended knees and say prayers of thankfulness to you for your father's grass they steal, because they owe it to you. Archie, what an ass you are, sitting here scribbling words on paper when you could be down seeing the really and truly bonniest beautifullest dearest woman in this bonny beautiful dear world. And so I will go down. But first, this letter and the price of a pint into Jimmy's patient hand. How long, I wonder, would he be willing to wait? He's daffing with the kitchen lassie. My, he's often broken His Majesty's regulations for us, carrying unstamped letters—we'll need to remember him, Rose, and be nice to him when we're old, old married folk even, for if it wasn't for him—oh, no, indeed, Archie Cameron, let not that thought enter your head, for nothing in this wide world would have stopped you loving Rose and marrying her. I've put by some minutes of that ten days, anyway. I'll be down on Jimmy's heels; I know it, I shouldn't, but there you are.

Your own

ARCHIE.

I met Thompson, the Aberdeen architect fellow, this morning. Now, what is he doing here a week before the Hall foundations are to be marked out? Would he be having a notion for little Margaret Davidson, do you think? Bless them, I hope so; I'm so happy I want everyone to be deep in love like me—though how on earth they can be when you're not available—but don't let them dare cast eyes at you! Meg will be a change for Thompson after that awful termagant who came here to see him in the autumn.

8

April 19
Mrs Macaskill, The Post-Office, to her cousin
Lizzie Macgregor, in New Zealand

MY DEAR COUSIN,

Just a few lines to let you know we are all fine here. You will be wondering at getting another letter from me so soon after the New Year, but I have news for you, cousin Lizzie. It is about my getting married to our old friend Shamus Munro that you will mind of. I know this will be a great surprise, but a lone woman is the better for a man about the place what with the state things are in at the present, air-raids and that. You will not be bothered with air-raids in New Zealand. It's only important countries that get them and Strathmazeran will likely get a lot so it's a good thing I'll have Shamus. He is a very clever man in every direction, though too honest and does not understand dirty tricks such as hawkers called MacAfee practise. He says too he always had a notion for me since we were at the school, and indeed, Lizzie, that's not yesterday. I'm keeping on the P.O. and Shamus will carry on with his engineering in the wash-house. It's to be a very quiet affair our marriage, on the 29th, the ceremony at the manse and then just a few friends to their tea here. I would have had the tea in the ben end but the fire smokes terrible so will just content ourselves with the kitchen. My niece Jenny, Rod's eldest lassie, you know, is to do it all. She's very handy about the house. We're not putting out invitations, just asking folks as we see them, but I wish you could be with us on the day. That's the worst of New Zealand, no dropping in on your old friends for a *ceilidh*. We thought of going to Auchmore for the week-end after the wedding, but Shamus is that full up of orders for the spring-cleaning at the manse and elsewhere we will not be going anywhere, just attending to business as usual, like in the War.

Shamus and me is both going to Rose Sinclair's wedding to Archie Cameron on the 24th. It will give us practice for our own performance. Of course, her marriage is to be a great affair. She is having cousins from the south for her maids, and Archie himself is having a cousin of his own from Inverartney for best man. I don't right know is it a son of his father's brother Hugh, but I'm thinking it is; you mind Hugh was married on a Macdonald from the west somewhere. Likely it will be their boy. What a presents they have gotten! As sure as death Jimmy Ishbel the Post was near dead carrying parcels up to Shirramore and Kerrow. I'm wondering how Rose will like living up at Kerrow. Her father will need a housekeeper. It's a great turn-up a marriage. However, it will likely be all for the best.

I'm thinking there's to be another wedding down at Cairnbeg. Margaret Davidson and that chap from Aberdeen were writing each other a lot, and now he's here staying at Cairnbeg, they say for the Hall but I'm wondering. He came on the 13th and there is nothing doing re Hall till to-morrow 20th. I can see you smiling to yourself, Lizzie. There's nothing public yet, but him and her were at the big Infirmary dance at Inverartney last Friday, him with an evening suit no less. Of course, he's a toff in a way and takes shootings, though very nice all the same. Margaret got a new dress from Edinburgh for it. You see a lot in the P.O., Lizzie. I would be sweirt to give it up.

Shamus and Mr Lockhart and Mr Thompson are to be starting off work on the new hall to-morrow 20th. I do not know right what they will be doing and Shamus did not say, but all in the glen is to be there. You will be saying, Steery times in Strathmazeran, Lizzie. Well, I think that is all of interest here at this time. We are very well suited with our new minister. He is to tie the knot for Shamus and me. Mrs Lockhart and me are at the cake and candy for the sale in the autumn which we are having for

the new hall here. As I told you, Shamus is at
the head of it. Mrs Lockhart was telling me how
she depended on Shamus to see her through the
spring cleaning, teasing mattrasses, beating carpets, and repairing all kinds of machinery. I
can assure you he's a great hand with the
machinery, he mended my old mangle beautiful.
Janet Colthart the maid at the hotel manse is
no lady, not like her mistress. When she heard
about Shamus and me says she to me says she:
'I wonder at you, Mrs Macaskill, trying marriage
again. Once bitten twice shy is what I would
think.' Jealousy is what's wrong with her. I
doubt she had a notion for Shamus herself. Now
I better close. I am sending this by air mail.
We're up to the nines in Strathmazeran I tell
you. So no more from your loving cousin

NELL.

9

April 22
Shamus Munro to Miss Janet Colthart

DEAR MISS COLTHART,

I am sorry hearing you are not pleased with
the mattrass I teased. I was thinking it should

be all right, I put the horse hair through the threshing-mill twice, case be. I am wondering terrible what can be wrong after that. There was not enough hair in it so I put in some wool, but seeing you are not pleased with it I will not charge for that. It was only broke wool anyway, but nice and clean. Mebbe when it is slept on a whiley it will come right. I am hoping so,

SHAMUS MUNRO.

Hoping you will be at wedding, 29th. Very quiet.

10

April 28

Janet Colthart, The Manse, to her sister
Mrs Katherine Hamilton, Peebles

MY DEAR KATE,

It was good of you to put yourself about over the hat I was needing for the Cameron-Sinclair wedding. At first I thought it very unsuitable, as I am not accustomed with a veil, but the mistress told me how smart it was so I just kept it. And am told it looked real *toney*. Of course

218

they see nothing here and are far behind the times, but all the same I could tell my own self it put all the others in the shade. That dark red is just my colour too. You should have seen some of the folk that were at the wedding! I think their clothes must have come out of the Ark, and the smell of camphor was something desperate. All the same, it was a great day for Strathmazeran.

The ceremony took place in the church, of course, and the week-end before I got hold of Willie Mitchell and him and me scrubbed the place out. Oh, it's not a very big kirk, you know, Katie, and we carried the hot water from the manse. We were right in the middle of it when who should come in but Miss Sinclair and her fiancé! She was most terrible pleased and wanted to send down the two Shirramore maids to give us a hand. But I would not allow her. To tell the truth, Katie, it was as much as I could do to keep Willie Mitchell at the job without having to manage two other folk, and Highlanders at that. I will say the place was as clean as gold when we finished, and I polished all the seats. Luckily we had plenty polish over from the spring cleaning. By the time the flowers were in, the place looked beautiful. It was a firm from the town that did the decorations, and yellow roses at that. It must have cost a bonny penny, but all in the best of taste. But fancy roses in April! Of course it is Miss Sinclair's name flower.

The church was full to capacity, and really, Katie, I never saw such a lovely bride. She wore white with silver roses patterned on it, and her maids were in gold. Young Mr Cameron is very good-looking too, and not near so haughty-looking as his father, who was there in full Highland dress, quite putting old Mr Sinclair in the shade. The minister looked real well too, for he wore his hood and I starched the bands myself, nice and stiff.

After the ceremony was over we all went up to Shirramore, and what a spread there was! Whisky and port in abundance and I'm sorry to say Willie Mitchell fell from grace again, as likewise did a good few more including James the Post. It's disgraceful the way men indulge themselves. No self-control at all. At night there was a big dance in Kerrow barn where they held the Christmas concert and dance for the hall. I didn't really mean to stay to the dance but was prevailed on by the Watts to accompany them as they didn't know many folk. I must say that I had a very enjoyable time, too, and only missed two dances. They are very keen on dancing here and like the old-fashioned ones best, which is a good thing, though they howl and yell all the time and when they dance an eightsome they make a most fearful noise, bawling and hooching like they were mad. Who do you think was never off the floor but that fool Shamus Munro who stole my tea-pot, and the shop wife. He was supposed to have lamed himself in a motor-car accident, but he seems to have had a quick recovery, though two-three weeks ago at the spring cleaning he made on he was awful bad. Alick Maclagan, who's supposed to be another invalid (rheumatics is what's ado with him, so he says), was another who never missed a dance. What do you think, Katie, Shamus Munro and the shop wife are getting married, and no rumour! Yes, to-morrow! In the study here, and the mistress is fussing away about getting the place extra clean for them. A fat lot they would know whether it was clean or dirty, and anyway I always thorough the study on Monday and I'm not to be put off my usual and do it out

on another day just for two ignorant Hieland
stots. But that's the mistress all over. She's too
fond of encouraging daft folk. She gave Shamus
all sorts of jobs to do at the cleaning, beating
carpets and so on. Of course I just had to do
them all over again. And she sent the mattress
off the second bedroom bed to him to get teased.
I wish you saw it when it came back. It was in
tatters and the stuffing was showing through all
round the edges. It was a good hair mattress in
its day but a bit thin. Munro stuffed it with
bits of old wool he found lying about, not very
clean either, and some chaff too if I'm not sore
cheat. I complained about it, and he wrote me
a p.c. saying he'd put it twice through the
threshing-mill. What can you do with a fool
of a man that will do a thing like that? If I
had him I'd put him through the mill, but he
took good care not to come near me but sent
the mattress back at dead of night and hid it in
the back porch for me to find when I opened
the door in the morning. There's plenty would
have been glad of the mattress before Munro got
his hands on it, but now I would not ask a brute
beast to lie down on it. I hope this will teach
the mistress better, but I doubt it. She laughed

like to end herself when I showed her the p.c.
Munro sent me. Fun's fun, Katie, and nobody
likes a good joke better than me, but waste is
not funny.

The hall is going on quite well now, which is
a wonder and likely it won't be for long as the
lambing is now on. The minister, of course,
thinks they are all saints here and that they'll
work all together with never a grumble but
what I say is *Them that'll do it will get it to do*.
There's a good lot working just now, but how
many will there be at the end? Oh, I've seen
it at work-parties and that.

Now I better close as it's my night for making
the tea for the hall workers. Oatcakes and cheese,
girdle scones and butter, and gingerbread is what
they're getting, and they're not bad off at
that.

Your affectionate sister,

JANET.

P.S.—Think of it, Katie, it's eight months
since I came here. I don't know where the
time's gone. Of course I'm always busy in
the house, but it's not for all that's going
on in this glen. Dead I call it. Not like
Peebles.

11

April 30

Margaret Davidson, Cairnbeg, to
John Thompson, Aberdeen

MY DEAR JOHNNY,

It was awfully nice of you to write such a fine long letter so soon after getting back to Aberdeen, where I'm sure you found your work all in arrears. Mother and I will be delighted to accept your invitation to visit Aberdeen this summer, though maybe you won't like us so much in the town as you do here. You know, we are country mice and not fashionable people at all. I wouldn't like you not to like us. Perhaps you'd better just come back to Cairnbeg.

I hope you got over the mingled effects of the Inverartney dance (oh, I did enjoy it!) and your fishing and your speechifying at the Hall ceremony. We never knew you were such a grand speaker. Alistair Og Maclagan was as proud of your few remarks as if he'd made them himself. After your departure I'm sorry to say he went off and caught a great whacking $3\frac{1}{2}$-pound trout on the setline. I expect that the next time he sees you he'll be letting on it was 6 lbs and he caught it on the Peter Ross. In fact, I wouldn't wonder a bit if he wrote you as much.

We have all recovered now from the big wedding, though there were a good few sore heads in the Strath the day after, for whisky flowed free amongst the men and the women drank port in a style befitting the teetotal drink they all call it. Yesterday Shamus Munro and Nell Macaskill got wed very sedately at the manse. It's a good thing for Shamus, though poor Nell will have her hands full with him. Perhaps she won't have so much time now to scrutinise every letter that comes into the post-office, and that wouldn't be a bad thing. She knows far more of everybody's affairs than they do themselves, but she can keep her own business dark enough.

You've no idea how bonny Strathmazeran is beginning to look. The heather-burning is all over and there's no smoke now to blur the clear hills. I wish you were here to see it instead of sitting in an office. May is the bonniest month for seeing our country. I always think our year really ends in April—to-day, in fact. But you must attend to your work and not run traipsing off into the wilds, mustn't you?

With kind thoughts from everyone here. If you've a spare moment, I'll be looking for a letter; I love getting letters, even though I know Nell Macaskill puts the queerest constructions on them.   MARGARET DAVIDSON.

12

April 30
Mrs Lockhart to Mrs Dalgarno, Edinburgh

MY DEAR MAISIE,

Thank you so much for your invitation for the Assembly week, but I'm afraid we'll have to say no, though I'd have loved seeing you again. But George is up to the eyes in his beloved hall, which is a-building at this very moment, and he doesn't want to leave the Strath till it's complete, which it won't be at the end of May. Why don't you come to see us instead? Do say yes. You'd love meeting the people here, and the glen itself grows bonnier every day.

We're just recovering from two weddings at the moment. One was, of course, Rose Sinclair's and Archie Cameron's. It was a most delightful event, and everyone who could attend was there.

226

Janet ordered poor Willackie Mitchell to scrub the church in preparation for it, and I don't think anything pleased Rose Sinclair so much as Janet's forethought. It really was nice of her, though Willackie is still wearing a cowed look. The reception was held at Shirramore, where we all repaired after the kirk ceremony. It was a lovely April day with larks singing and peewits swooping above the fields. The sun shone on the fresh green of the larches, and altogether it was as darling a day for a wedding as ever I saw.

The next marriage was that of my good friend Shamus Munro to Mrs Macaskill at the Shop. It took place yesterday as ever was in the study here, and really, Maisie, I'm still laughing over it. Some time ago Shamus lured Mrs M. into giving him all her savings to finance a mad scheme of his for collecting scrap-iron. Then he disappeared, and the distracted Mrs Macaskill at last called in George's aid. By dint of careful inquiry and firm handling Shamus was induced to come home. He had been cheated shamefully out of every penny and was afraid to come back. However, he did come, and now Mrs Macaskill and he are married. I don't know what transpired between them to bring about this beautiful and romantic result, but soon after his return Shamus wrote George a lovely letter expressing deep contrition for his ongoings and saying that Nell and he were to get married—if George had no objections! So yesterday they appeared and were duly wed at the desk, which I polished specially myself in their honour, owing to Janet's deep disapproval of the whole thing. Alistair Og Maclagan was best man, and a glaikit-looking young woman, niece of the bride, was bridesmaid. Shamus appeared clad in a truly magnificent navy-blue coat thick enough to go to the North Pole in, and he wore gloves put on back to front—fastened on the backs of his hands instead of on the palms. He refused to take either coat or gloves off, and his fumblings with the ring were truly dreadful, but his blushing and rather complacent bride watched him admiringly throughout. She herself looked very nice, I thought, in a brown coat and frock and a positively skittish hat. She has such a sweet gentle trusting face, too! Shamus and herself were so overcome with shyness they would hardly say a word, and if Alistair hadn't pushed and shoved them both about they'd never have got their responses out at all. When George asked Shamus whether he took this woman for his lawful wedded wife, Shamus—still in his gloves—grasped Nell's hand firmly and simpered, whilst Alistair bawled out : 'Of course he does ; come on, Shamus, man, tell Mr Lockhart you do.'

'What do I do ?' asked Shamus, in an agonised fashion. However, by dint of all our advice we got them safely married and had tea with them afterwards in Mrs Macaskill's kitchen, which was already festooned with strange appliances belonging to Shamus, who made several attempts to tell me something about Janet, a tea-pot, and the mattrass, as he calls it, but was always cut off short by Alistair. This idle invalid acted as if it was his house, and bossed Nell unmercifully.

Janet has taken this romance very badly, owing to the fact that I gave Shamus little jobs to do at the spring cleaning just to help him regain his self-respect. I gave him an old mattress to tease, and he didn't make just a professional job of it. Janet was angry, and he wrote her a note to say that he'd put the mattress through the threshing-mill so it should be all right ! He also made a few improvements to its stuffing by shoving in bits of wool he had lying about. Janet was livid with rage, and very annoyed with me for laughing. It was an old thing, anyway; but fancy putting a mattress through the threshing-mill! Naturally it's a complete wreck—the mattress, I mean. I've a good mind to offer it to Shamus as a wedding present. Then he'd be not so much hoist with his own petard as bruised with his own stuffing.

I know that you'll be interested to hear our hall is going on and that George's voluntary labour is coming up to scratch far better than I expected. But really the schoolmaster and an Aberdeenshire compatriot of his are responsible for the smooth working of the scheme. They drew up time-tables and got everyone to put his name down for work. Then they stuck up the lists in plain view in the shop and at the church door, so that everyone will know the defaulters if there are any. It has been an excellent scheme. We had our architect, Mr Thompson from Aberdeen, come along for the opening ceremony—if you can call pacing out the foundations the opening. By the way, Janet hints that there's a budding romance between Mr Thompson and Margaret Davidson at Cairnbeg. Janet reads too many novels. But it *is* true he seems to like coming here for quite inadequate reasons, and he stays much longer than is really essential to his purpose.

The only project of George's which has come flop so far is the garden. He set his heart on making the manse garden perhaps not blossom like the rose but at least provide all the vegetables we need. Willie Mitchell and himself delved it over, but the rabbits have descended on their handiwork and eaten the plants they put down. Before he does anything more George'll need to make the place rabbit-proof. Fortunately, Janet and I have a private scheme by which we've made arrangements to get all the greens we want from the Watts, the new folk at Croft Roy, who are throughly practical people. Already we're getting our milk and eggs there, which has angered Alistair Og very much, since we used to deal with him. But it's entirely his own fault we left him. You could never depend on getting *what* you wanted *when* you wanted it. It's a pity the dear Highlanders are so unbusiness-like, but, oh, I do like them in spite of it.

I can hardly believe we've been eight months here. How happily the time has gone past; and now we're looking forward to the summer, when I hope you'll come north and see for your-

self what a dear place Strathmazeran is. Somehow I feel as if our first period here had ended,
and now another is beginning. So many things
have happened. We have made heaps of friends.
Both of us feel at home.

With much love,

your affectionate friend,

ALICE.

13

April 30

Rev. George Lockhart to Andrew Duncan,
Edinburgh

MY DEAR FRIEND,

Many thanks for your kind letter. You ask
are we still happy in Strathmazeran. Ah, here
we have found a haven whose power to make us
happy increases. In a city one labours without
end, but there are so many people, the difficulties
are so vast, one seems to make no impression,
and the result of one's work is never visible, as it
is here. Here I have few people, and my work
is light, but my joy in it is great.

For the thing that has made me happiest I
take no credit, if indeed the Christian should

ever take credit for using to his fellows' advantage the powers and opportunities that are granted him. But it was storm, the malevolence of nature as manifested in snowy gales, which solved the most grievous problem that confronted me and was like to embitter the whole life of this quiet sparsely populated glen. I refer to the quarrel between my ruling elders. As I told you, litigation between them was pending. Then suddenly a storm came upon the wings of tempest—can one doubt that the thing men call chance is guided and controlled by a greater Power than man can conceive of, whose tools are the furious winds, and waves, and floods? We live, my dear friend, in a moral world. One of my quarrelling elders went out in the storm to tend his flock. The blizzard overwhelmed him, for he is no longer young, and he must inevitably have perished had not the son of his enemy found him and brought him home by a feat of superhuman endurance. Now my ruling elders are at amity. Just the other day I married their children here in our little church, which, though it had no red cloth at the door and no press photographers, was filled to overflowing with every soul in the glen who could attend. I have seldom seen so handsome a couple. It was a pleasure of the deepest to see them there, to know that in their happiness an old wicked feud was irrevocably destroyed. I know they will be happy, I pray they may be wise and in God's good time when their own children face the world that they may remember to be tolerant and cherish no rancour against any man. Alas, man never learns save by bitter experience. We are all more doubting than Didymus. We must feel the nails in our own flesh before we believe that they can hurt, and wound, and tear. All the wisdom man gains is from sore experience in doing wrong. The old Adam rules us still.

But I have had another wedding, which was celebrated here only yesterday, very quietly, as befitted the marriage of older people—in the manse study. Shamus Munro, concerning whom also I wrote to you in the past, grew so bold with conceit of his own abilities that nothing would please him but he must turn himself into a great scrap-metal merchant, with which intention he persuaded the gullible postmistress and proprietrix of the local store here to advance him money. He was, of course, speedily cheated out of every penny. Mrs Macaskill's entire life-savings were taken from him. I dealt very firmly with Shamus, and as he has returned to the Strath in a contrite spirit he may have learned his lesson. I say *may*. Not long after his return he informed me that there was a purpose of marriage between himself and Mrs Macaskill and asked me to perform the ceremony, which as I have told you I did yesterday. I feel sure that Mrs Macaskill will exercise a more restraining influence over his exuberant spirit now that they are man and wife than she was able or inclined to do in the past. She appeared in the past to set Shamus on something of a pedestal, from which even his losing her little all in the way of worldly wealth did not remove him. But marriage is an institution admirably fitted to reveal a person's feet of clay. Yet I wonder if even marriage will keep Shamus down for long. His scrap-iron misadventure assuredly will not. And still, he contributes to the gaiety of our lives, and even I would be sad to see him turned to pedestrian ways.

My new parishioner Watt, with his wife and family now arrived from Aberdeenshire, where they remained until he made their new home ready for them, is like to prove a tower of strength, though he is not what I would call a regular church-goer. But his wife is very constant. Nevertheless, despite his frequent absence from a place of worship on Sabbath, he strikes me as a man of good character, who will prove his worth here in no small measure, though he is inclined to be hard and somewhat dictatorial, which his neighbours must in the long run resent. At the moment they are mostly charmed with him, being, like the Athenians, great runners after new things, and especially new people. Watt has asked me to assist him to organise bulk-buying amongst the crofters. He has a scheme for getting the women of the Strath to knit for some large firm. And he is eager to start a branch of the Beekeepers' Association. In all these manifold projects he has, as I am perfectly aware, got Number One well in mind. I care not for that so long as the benefits he obtains bring advantage to others. The native people here are very charming. One would never accuse Watt, with his harsh speech and forceful methods, of charm. But he has a directness and vigour of purpose, a coolness of judgment, and an amazing ability to organise which are sorely needed amongst my people and which, properly applied, will serve them well. Not least of Watt's merits in my wife's eyes is that he has undertaken to supply her with milk, butter, cream and eggs all the year round, and fruit and vegetables in their season should we require them, which of course we shall not, since the manse garden is in my special care.

It is a constant astonishment to me that here in the country we are far worse supplied with country fare—milk, butter, cream, eggs, honey, fruit, and vegetables—than we were in the city of Edinburgh. I do not like milk out of the tin, which, alas, we have been consuming a great deal this past winter. Even now in the full flush of spring milk is still scarce. There is some question of calves sucking their mothers which I do not fully understand as yet, though Watt explained the matter very lucidly, exposing the fallacies of his neighbours' economics in masterly fashion.

I come last of all to the project which, outside the spiritual welfare of my flock, is nearest and dearest to my heart; I refer to the village hall. Here again I must proclaim my indebtedness to Watt and to Mackie the schoolmaster, both of whom have assisted me to falsify the fears of many people, including my own wife, lest we fail in our plan to build the hall by voluntary labour. I shall not weary you with details of our negotiations. Suffice it to say that we laid the foundations of the hall ten days ago. The money it will cost is easily within our ability to raise. The Carnegie Trustees are, of course, an enormous boon. Now the work of erection goes on apace, despite the fact that it is lambing-time and therefore a busy season on the farms, where work on the arable land also goes on at speed. Each man who comes to work on the hall vies with his neighbours in friendly emulation, and ere long the hall will have changed from a fond dream to solid reality.

I can scarcely believe that it is eight months since we came here. Eight busy months have sped like a dream. That is a long time out of an old man's life. It carries him a great way on his journey towards the bourne from which no traveller returns. And yet I do not grudge the speed with which time has flown. We have been happy. Our lives have been full, our lines are cast in pleasant places, beside the still waters. Happiness is a strange cordial which makes glad the heart of man, and strengthens him to face the ending of his days. It is misery that makes

238

men cling to life and fear the future. How wise Tinker Bunyan was to make his pilgrims cross the Delectable Mountains ere they reached the dark river!

I love Strathmazeran. It has made itself home for me. I feel as if I belonged to its woods and hills, its people too. Perhaps that is because I was a country boy, though long in city pent. They tell me that summer is glorious here. All seasons are dear when joy and useful labour fill their hours. The winter of my life has come, each summer I look forward to may be the last. It is doubly sweet, therefore. And ah, how well blessed I have been by a fortunate fate which brought me here. When you come to visit us, as you have so often promised, and as I hope with all my heart you may do soon, summer will be coming over these great hills like a young man rejoicing in his strength, over these great dark hills which soon, I trust, I may show you with pride as if I owned them all alone. I long for you to come. We have many things to speak of, things old and new.

Now, dear friend, enough of myself and Strathmazeran. What I have written shows but a pale shadow of this place and its people, who

are strangely mine; Shamus, Alistair Og, quarrelling elders, Watt, Mackie, all I have spoken of
in all my letters seem linked to me and to each
other in a common bond. We are very strangely
one place, and one people. But now, no more
of place or people. The long dusk is drawing
towards the blackness of night. Strathmazeran
goes gently to sleep as I end this long letter. Its
lights are few and scattered, and dear to me, and
the hills are very dark. Strathmazeran sends you
good-night, good-night and, for the time being,
good-bye.

      Good-night, my dear old friend,

                GEORGE LOCKHART.

THE END